IQ
TESTS

A LITTLE GIANT® BOOK

IQ TESTS

PHILIP J. CARTER
& KENNETH A. RUSSELL

STERLING
New York

STERLING
New York

An Imprint of Sterling Publishing
387 Park Avenue South
New York, NY 10016

STERLING and the distinctive Sterling logo are registered trademarks
of Sterling Publishing Co., Inc.

ISBN 978-1-4549-1177-7

Library of Congress CIP Data is available.

Distributed in Canada by Sterling Publishing
c/o Canadian Manda Group, 165 Dufferin Street
Toronto, Ontario, Canada M6K 3H6
Distributed in the United Kingdom by GMC Distribution Services
Castle Place, 166 High Street, Lewes, East Sussex, England BN7 1XU
Distributed in Australia by Capricorn Link (Australia) Pty. Ltd.
P.O. Box 704, Windsor, NSW 2756, Australia

For information about custom editions, special sales, and premium and
corporate purchases, please contact Sterling Special Sales at
800-805-5489 or specialsales@sterlingpublishing.com.

Manufactured in China

2 4 6 8 10 9 7 5 3 1

www.sterlingpublishing.com

Contents

Introduction

Intelligence is the ability to adapt to new situations, think abstractly, and comprehend complex ideas. IQ is the abbreviation for Intelligence Quotient. The word "quotient" means the results of dividing one quantity by another.

An intelligence test (IQ Test) is a standardized test designed to measure human intelligence as distinct from attainments. The aim of the seventeen tests in this book is to give your brain a thorough mental workout and to familiarize yourself with the various types of questions you are likely to encounter when taking a supervised test.

The questions are challenging, and deliberately so, as this is the only way to boost your performance and increase your brainpower.

But above all, the tests are designed to entertain. It is, therefore, up to you as to how you wish to use the book—either to test yourself or your friends on each test against the clock, or to simply dip into the book at random and attempt whichever of the hundreds of questions takes your fancy at the time.

It's your choice, but whichever way you choose to use the book, have fun, enjoy the questions, and happy solving!

For readers wishing to assess their performance, a time limit of 90 minutes is allowed for each test.

Use the following scoring table for each test:

Score	Rating
36–40	Exceptional
31–40	Excellent
25–30	Very Good
19–20	Good
14–18	Average

1. Read clockwise to figure out this sixteen-letter word. Only alternate letters are shown, and you have to find the starting point.

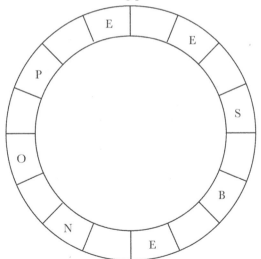

2. What number should replace the question mark?

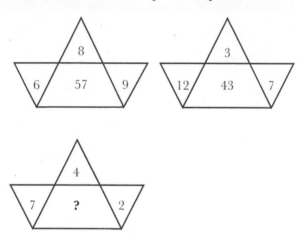

3. Only one set of letters below can be arranged into a five-letter English word. Can you find the word?

BYRDI   TONET

NRCOL   PUITN

HUTME   LEBIT

TINOL   RUGNE

BEHAD

4.

 is to

as

 is to:

A.   B.   C.   D.

5. Which three-letter word forms two other words that are unrelated in meaning when "LESS" and "NESS" are added to the end? For example, SOUND: SOUNDLESS, SOUNDNESS.

Clue: Foolish deponent

6. Which number is the odd one out?

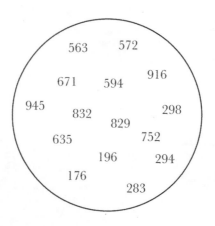

7. I create a happy sound on my entire journey to a place of monetary deposit. What am I doing?

8. Which word comes closest in meaning to METE? CARRY, ADJOIN, COORDINATE, ALLOT, PARODY

9. Only ten letters of the alphabet do not appear in this grid. What ten-letter phrase can they be arranged to spell out?

P	Z	B	G
M	O	K	J
F	W	Q	X
Y	V	R	D

Clue: Cape Canaveral

10. What number comes next in this sequence?

483, 759, 264, 837, ?

11. What symbol should replace the question mark?

A.   B.   C.   D.

12. One letter in each word of a well-known saying has been changed. What is the saying?

TAPE TIE PULL MY TOE CORNS

13. To what number should the missing hand on the clock point?

1.

2.

3.

4.

14. Fill in the blanks with the same seven letters in the same order so that the sentence makes complete sense.

A _____ chef was _____ to serve the meal because he had _____.

15. LEA : PIE
SAP :

    (a) BAT
    (b) WAG
    (c) BOW
    (d) WET
    (e) YET

16. What, in connection with this question, is the next number below?

4, 13, 19, 21, 29, ?

17. What phrase is suggested below?

```
SH
TT
RG
EN
```

18. What number should appear in the circle with the question mark?

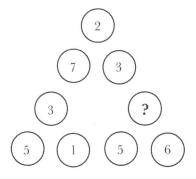

19. What face should replace the question mark?

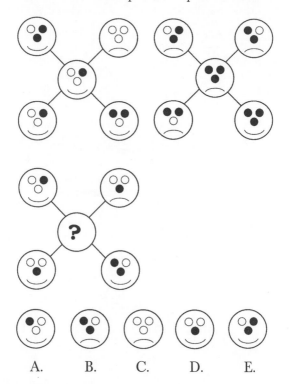

A.   B.   C.   D.   E.

20. Fill in the missing word to complete the crossword.

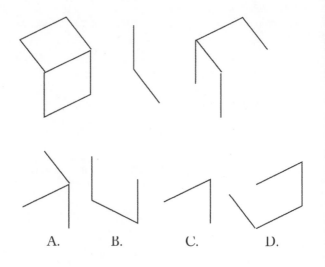

A.   B.   C.   D.

22. EUPHORIA is to BLISS as
MELANCHOLY is to:

(a) BAWDY
(b) UNSEEMLY
(c) DESPAIR
(d) NEGATE
(e) RIBALD

23. Place two of the four-letter groups together to make a word.

RIAL - SYCO - TUTO - PANT - PLAT

24. Which pentagon continues the series?

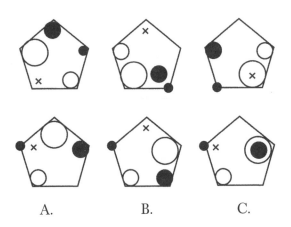

A.

B.

C.

25. Find a one-word anagram in CREAM ELK.

26. Simplify $\dfrac{5}{11} \div \dfrac{25}{22}$.

27. Trace out a ten-letter word in any direction, using each letter once only.

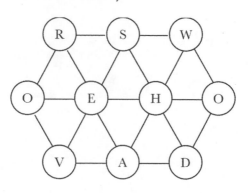

28. Simplify $\dfrac{725}{1000}$ as a fraction.

29. Which word means the fear of MICE?

    (a) ANEMOPHOBIA
    (b) MUSOPHOBIA
    (c) BAROPHOBIA
    (d) POTOPHOBIA
    (e) OCHOPHOBIA

30. What is the meaning of PRANDIAL?

    (a) BREAKFAST
    (b) TEATIME
    (c) DINNER
    (d) SUPPER
    (e) SNACKS

31. A word can be placed inside the parentheses that has the same meaning as the words outside. What is it?

TAR (_ _ _ _ _) SET UP

32. If $4 \times 4 = 20$,
then $5 \times 6 = $?

33. Which circle's letters cannot be rearranged into a six-letter word?

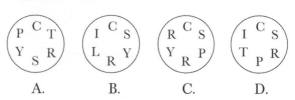

A.   B.   C.   D.

34. Which number should replace the question mark?

6	8	17	21
13	1	9	10
3	15	4	?
4	6	4	5

35. What is the opposite of NEOPHYTE?

(a) EARTHLY
(b) NOVICE
(c) ANCIENT
(d) EXPERT
(e) STARLIKE

36. What number should replace the question mark?

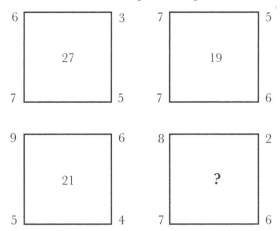

37. Which animal does not fit with the others?

(a) CHAMOIS
(b) TIERCEL
(c) IMPALA
(d) FENNEC
(e) GERBIL
(f) JERBOA

38. Place the letters in the grid to make a flower and a fish.

G O P P P P U Y Y

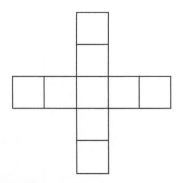

39. What is the mathematical sign for "identical with"?

(a) [ ]
(b) >
(c) ≡
(d) /
(e) <

40. Complete the word.

$$_ _ C K J _ _$$

1. Change SEPTEMBER to JULY. The asterisks in each word are common to the word above it.

```
        SEPTEMBER
          * * * *
_ _ _ _       _ _         Clue: Hygenic
    * * *
_ _   * * *   _ _ _ _     Clue: Anthropod
_ _ _       _ _           Clue: Numerous
    JULY
    * *
```

2. What number should replace the question mark?

2	9	7
10	**?**	12
8	13	5

3. Add one letter, not necessarily the same letter, to each word to find eight words that all have something in common.

MAT, SEW, ART, SAG, BAN, FAN, ICE

4. Which day is two days before the day after the day three days after the day before Tuesday?

SUNDAY
MONDAY
TUESDAY
WEDNESDAY
THURSDAY
FRIDAY
SATURDAY

5. Which of the numbered figures is the odd one out?

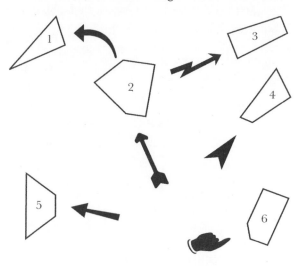

6. The following clue leads to what pair of rhyming words?

SKILLFUL ROBBERY

7. A pancake can be sliced into four pieces in any number of ways by using two cuts. One example is shown below. What is the maximum number of pieces that can be obtained from a pancake using three cuts?

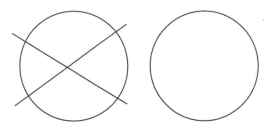

8. How many lines appear below?

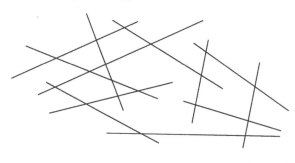

9. What number should replace the question mark?

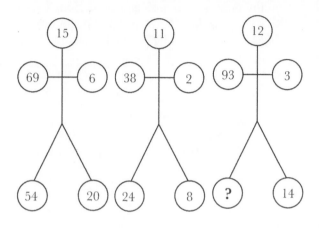

10. All widgets are green. Everything green has a hole in the middle. Some things that are green have a jagged edge. Therefore:
1. All widgets have a hole in the middle.
2. Everything with a jagged edge is a widget.
3. Neither of the above is true.
4. Both the above are true.

11. What number should replace the question mark?

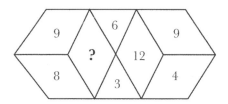

12. Unscramble these four anagrammed words to determine what they have in common.

OGLED, WROTE, CLEATS, PELMET

13. Which is the odd one out?

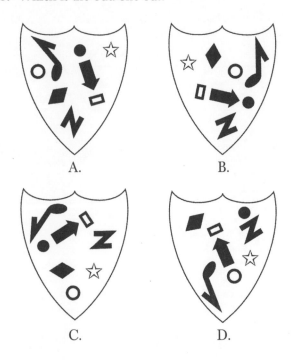

A.

B.

C.

D.

14. Insert the letters of the phrase FAMILIES MASS SALE into the empty spaces below, using each letter once to complete a palindromic sentence—one that reads the same backwards and forwards. For example: MADAM, I'M ADAM.

_ A _ _ _ _ S _ _ _ _ _ _ _ _ S _ _ _

Clue: Relatively altruistic

15. "The chance of exposure to the adverse consequences of future events." Which word fits closest to the above definition?

(a) SPECULATION
(b) DANGER
(c) RISK
(d) WORRY
(e) HALLUCINATION

16. What number continues this sequence?

8960, 6720, 3360, 840, 630, ?

17. What number should replace the question mark?

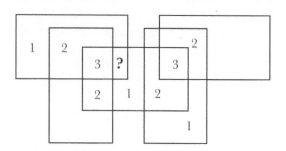

18. Which two words below are closest in meaning?

AUTHENTIC, GERMANE, FOREIGN,
GENTLE, PRODIGIOUS, COGNATE

19. What well-known proverb is opposite in meaning
to the proverb "Too many cooks spoil the broth"?

20. Place three of the two-letter groups together to form a fruit.

OR – LY – AN – EE – GO – CH

21. Which is the missing square?

A.   B.   C.   D.

22. Which word will fit in front of these words to make new words?

$(\_\_\_\_)$

BOOT
POT
ASS
DAW
HAMMER

23. What number should replace the question mark?

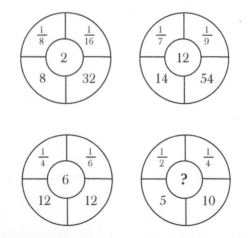

24. There is a system for pricing the menu. What would oysters cost?

MENU	
SOUP	$18
SALAD	$23
ROAST BEEF	$41
ICE CREAM	$36
COFFEE	$27

25. Which number should replace the question mark?

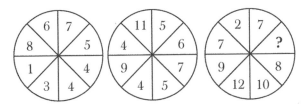

26. If the missing letters in the circle below are correctly inserted they will form an eight-letter word. The word will not have to be read in a clockwise direction, but the letters are consecutive. What is the word and missing letters?

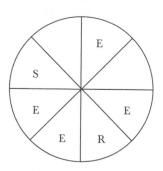

27. What is the surface area of this tennis ball?

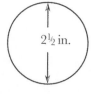

(a) 17.635 sq. in.
(b) 18.635 sq. in.
(c) 19.635 sq. in.
(d) 20.635 sq. in.
(e) 21.635 sq. in.

28. What number should replace the question mark?

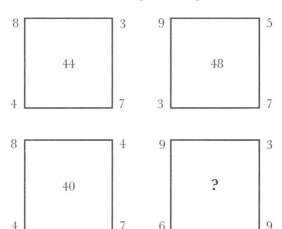

29. Which word means the same as VIBRATO?

(a) LUSTROUS
(b) EXCITING
(c) THROBBING
(d) SOFTLY
(e) STATIONARY

30. What number should replace the question mark?

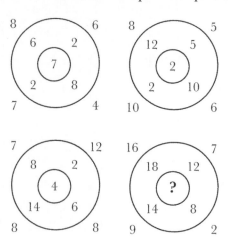

31. The vowels have been omitted from this quotation. Can you replace them?

T S W S F T H R T H T K N W S H S W N C H L D

32. Place the letters in the grid to form a nautical person and a mineral.

A A C E F I P
L O R R R D

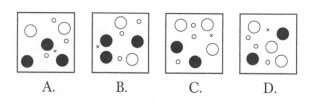

34. Which of the boxes below is most like the box on the right?

A.   B.   C.   D.

35. Fill in the missing letters to make a nine-letter word starting from a corner square and spiraling into the center.

U		E
	E	R
E	T	A

36. Which of the following is always associated with HAMSTRING?

(a) PIGS
(b) BACON
(c) TENNIS RACQUETS
(d) DINNER
(e) TENDON

37. What number should replace the question mark?

7 11 20 ? 61 97 146

38. Rearrange the two five-letter words to form a ten-letter word meaning "trader with Native Americans."

MOOCH CANER

39. By moving through the doorways, spell out an eight-letter word. Each letter may only be used once.

40. Fill in the missing letters to make a nine-letter word starting from a corner square and continuing in a spiral to the center.

O		E
W	S	R
O	L	

1. By joining corners and not counting rotations and reflections it is only possible to dissect a pentagon into three triangles one way and a hexagon three different ways. Both are illustrated below:

In how many ways is it possible to dissect a heptagon?

2. Complete the word below that contains a unique trigraph—i.e., three consecutive letters which appear in no other English word.

_ _ _ _ KSG _ _ _ _ _

3. Find just one reason for arranging the following words into three groups, each containing three words:

MONKEY, LOANED, CORNER, LONGER, BLONDE, SPONGE, HORNET, WONDER, BRONZE

4. What completes the below sequence?

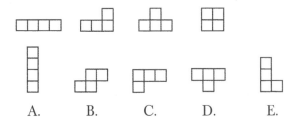

A.   B.   C.   D.   E.

5. LARGO : SLOW
PIANO :

A. SMOOTH; B. LOUD; C. SOFT;
D. PLAY; E. BRISK

6. What number should replace the question mark?

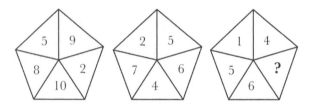

7. Tom beats Joe at pool but loses to Sue. Hilary usually wins against Joe, sometimes against Tom, but never against Sue. Who is the weakest player?

8. Which number is the odd one out?

3628, 2426, 4146, 1448

9. Working clockwise, take one letter from each circle in turn to spell out two synonyms.

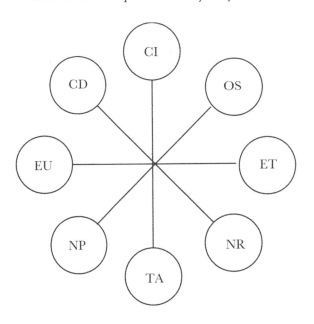

NOTE: Each word starts in a different circle.

10. The die is rolled one face to Square 2, and so on—one face at a time to Squares 3-4-5-6. Which number will appear on the top face in Square 6?

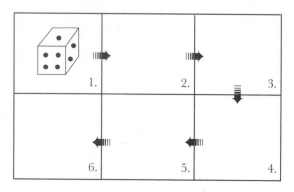

11. Solve the cryptic clue below. The answer is a ten-letter anagram contained within the clue:

ESCORT A
MAN UNSTEADILY
TO CALIFORNIAN
CITY

12. Insert the numbers 1–5 in the circles, using each number once, in such a way that for any particular circle the sum of the number in the circles connected directly to it add up to the value allocated to the number inside the circle in accordance with the table below:

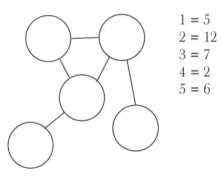

$1 = 5$
$2 = 12$
$3 = 7$
$4 = 2$
$5 = 6$

EXAMPLE:

$1 = 14 \ (4 + 7 + 3)$
$4 = 8 \ (7 + 1)$
$7 = 5 \ (4 + 1)$
$3 = 1$

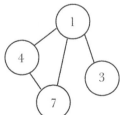

13. If meat in a river (3 in 6) is T(HAM)ES, can you find a thin rope in an instrument (4 in 9)?

14. Arrange the letters in the squares below to find two nine-letter words that are antonyms.

		L	A	R
R	G	E	H	G
E	N	T	I	C
E	C	I		

15. Insert a word in the parentheses that means the same as the definitions outside the parentheses:

HASTEN (   ) GRASSLIKE PLANT

16.

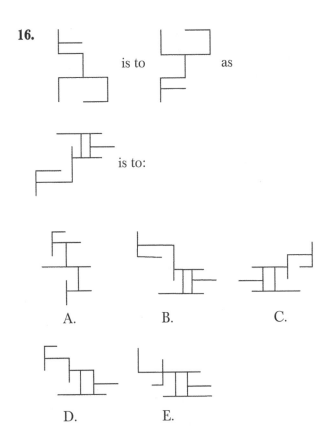

17. Arrange these words in alphabetical order.

ABOUND
ABSCOND
ABALONE
ABDOMEN
ABDICATE
ABROGATES
ABANDON

18. What number should replace the question mark?

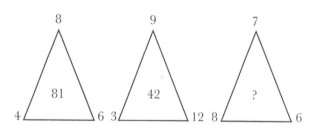

19. The words BLACK and WHITE are antonyms. What two words, one rhyming with BLACK and one with WHITE, are also antonyms?

20. Which is the missing square?

A.

B.

C.

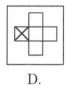
D.

21. What number should replace the question mark?

Simplify: $5 + 8 - 4 + 9 \times 2 + 7 = ?$

22. Find pairs of letters to form four four-letter musical instruments—one pair is not used.

BA	HA	LU
TE	FE	OB
FI	OE	TU

23. Find a six-letter word made up of only the four following letters:

ON
IP

24. Place two of the three-letter groups together to form an article of clothing.

SOC - TER - COA - JER - KIT - SHI - KIN - RTY

25. Which two words are similar in meaning?

PLUNDER, CHARM, JOSH, WEAN,
TEASE, CHANGE

26. Which of these is the odd one out?

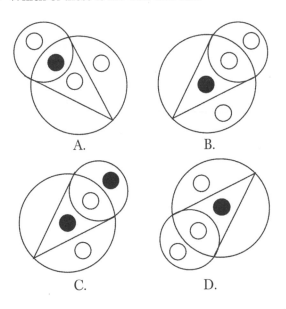

A.

B.

C.

D.

27. Which diagram continues the sequence?

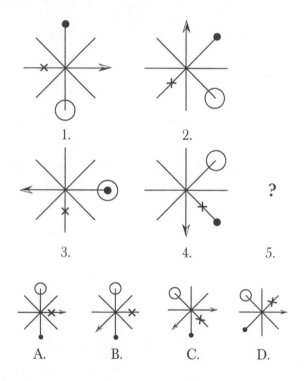

1.

2.

?

3.

4.

5.

A.

B.

C.

D.

28. Rearrange the letters in each set to form the name of a plant.

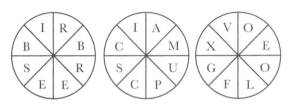

29. Find the missing word that will fit the rule of the example below.

CONE (NICK) KRIS
LISP (_ _ _ _) ETON

30. A stone is dropped over the edge of a cliff. After 5 seconds how many feet has it fallen?

(a) 280 ft.
(b) 320 ft.
(c) 400 ft.
(d) 480 ft.
(e) 500 ft.

31. Starting at a corner square, move along a spiral route and find the rule for the numbering to replace the question mark.

32	28	34	30
26	42	38	36
30	36	?	32
24	40	34	38

32. How many revolutions are made by a 28-inch bicycle wheel over 1 mile?

(a) 620
(b) 720
(c) 820
(d) 920
(e) 1020

33. Draw the next figure in this series.

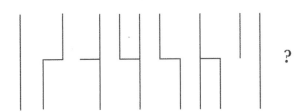

?

34. What is the mathematical sign for infinity?

(a) ≮

(b) ∞

(c) Δ

(d) ::

(e) ∝

35. Fill in the blanks to find three islands:

```
_ H _ I _ T _ A _
_ A _ R _ T _ U _
_ A _ K _ A _ D
```

36. Find a three-letter word that completes all three words on the left-hand side and prefixes all three words on the right-hand side.

HAS		DON
ROT	(_ _ _)	PIN
FAT		ANT

37. On which target have 185 points been scored?

A.   B.   C.   D.

38. Which of the following is always part of SAUERKRAUT?

CHEESE, HOT WATER, MILK, BUTTER, CABBAGE

39. Place a word in the parentheses that when placed at the end of the first word makes a word and when placed in front of the second word also makes a word.

QUARTER (_ _ _ _) HAND

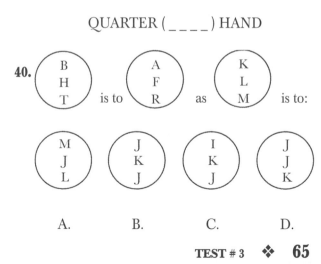

40.

| B H T | is to | A F R | as | K L M | is to: |

| M J L | J K J | I K J | J J K |
| A. | B. | C. | D. |

1. Which is the odd one out?

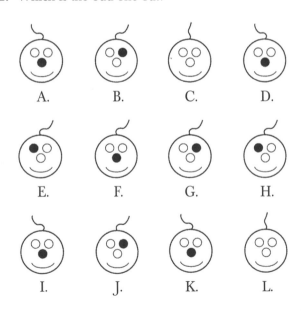

2. Solve the anagram in parentheses to correctly complete the quotation.

Failure is the only opportunity to begin again, more (leniently gilt).   *Henry Ford*

3. Pair the eight words below to form four hyphenated words. Use each word once only.

GROUP, STILL, TYPING, AGE, STOCK, SIZE, BLOOD, TWIN

4. Mitzi has $800 to spend. She spends ⅖ of the $800 on clothes, 0.425 of the $800 on jewelry, and writes out a check for $240 for a new watch. What is her financial situation at the end of the day?

5. Which word is opposite in meaning to OPTIMUM?

ANTITHESIS, UNORIGINAL, LEAST, STARK, CHASTE

6. What is the missing number?

5	3	8	4	9	6	8
8	6	6	1	8	4	?
3	2	7	6	8	7	3

7. GAZEBO   ACCEDE   VERIFY

Which girl's name continues the above sequence?

A. EUNICE,   B. AGATHA,   C. JOANNE,
D. INGRID

8. Solve the two anagrams to produce a well-known saying.

9. When the below is folded to form a cube, just one of the following can be produced. Which one?

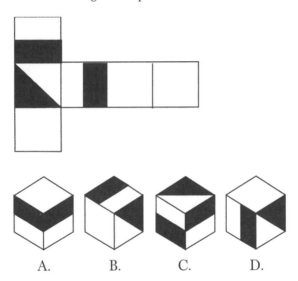

A.   B.   C.   D.

10. If 9L of a C is 9 lives of a cat, can you decode the following?

10P in C

11. Solve the clues to find four six-letter words. The same three letters are represented by XYZ in each word.

	Clue
X Y Z _ _ _	Clue: Fleet
_ X Y Z _ _	Clue: Heat
_ _ X Y Z _	Clue: Beguiles
_ _ _ X Y Z	Clue: Remove defensive capability

12. What number should replace the question mark?

13. The word SOLO appears only once in this grid in a straight line. Can you find it? It may appear horizontally, vertically or diagonally, backwards or forwards.

S	O	L	S	L	O	S	O
S	O	S	O	S	O	O	S
O	O	S	O	S	L	O	O
O	S	O	L	S	O	O	O
S	O	S	L	S	L	L	O
L	S	L	O	O	S	O	S
O	O	O	S	S	O	O	L
O	S	L	L	O	S	L	O

14. Which is the odd one out?

A.

B.

C.

D.

E

15. Spiral clockwise to find a ten-letter word. You must find the starting point and provide the missing letters. The word you are looking for starts and finishes with the same two letters.

16. We all have the ____1____ to put our ____2____ to even more use by ____3____ new avenues, experiences, and ____4____ adventures.

Select the correct words from the choices below to correctly complete the above statement.
1. privilege, sense, capacity, preference, imagination
2. computers, money, ability, brain, vitality
3. exploring, finding, arranging, touring, crossing
4. dangerous, modern, subtle, discreet, learned

17. Insert a girl's name into the bottom line and complete the three-letter words.

H	C	F	F	A	E	S	T
I	U	U	O	L	G	I	I

18. What number should replace the question mark?

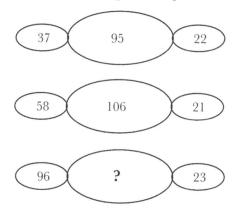

19. DYNAMIC (ADORN) PROFUSE

Using the same rules as the example above, what word should appear in the parentheses below?

REPORTS (_ _ _ _ _) LIBERTY

20. What well-known phrase is indicated below?

```
C O B   L T
C O   A L T
C   B A L T
C O B A   T
C O B A L
```

21. What is the total of the numbers on the reverse of these dice?

22. Which of these is the odd one out?

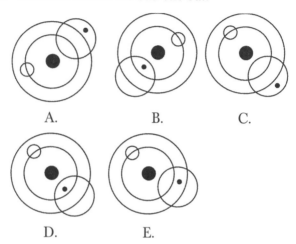

A. B. C.

D. E.

23. Which of these is not an anagram of currency?

(a) ZETQULEA
(b) YOMASED
(c) DASRUCO
(d) VILBAOR
(e) TATRES
(f) TERECSES

24. Find a one-word anagram in:

SORE CAT

25. Place four of the three-letter groups together to make two six-letter words.

SUT - TIC - NAU - TIN - HER - MET - SEA - MIT

26. Fill in the blank spaces to spell out these dances.

_ I _ T _ R _ U _
_ U _ D _ I _ L _
_ O _ O _ A _ S _

27. Which two words have opposite meanings?

LADYLIKE, SUCCINCT, TURBULENT COMMODIOUS, HOYDENISH, EMACIATED

28. If the missing letters in the two circles below are correctly inserted they will form synonymous words. The words do not have to be read in a clockwise direction, but the letters are consecutive. What are the words and missing letters?

29. What roman numeral should replace the question mark?

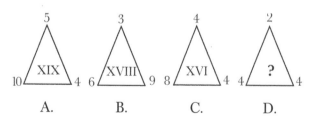

A. B. C. D.

30. What number should replace the question mark?

  7   17 $8\frac{1}{2}$ $14\frac{1}{4}$ 10 $11\frac{1}{2}$?

31. What is the meaning of MANTILLA?

(a) TROUSERS
(b) SHIP
(c) DRESS
(d) LOGANBERRIES
(e) SCARF

32. There are only five regular solids with symmetrical faces. Which one of these has twenty faces?

(a) ICOSAHEDRON
(b) DODECAHEDRON
(c) CUBE
(d) TETRAHEDRON
(e) OCTAHEDRON

33. How many degrees is this angle?

(a) 105°
(b) 110°
(c) 115°
(d) 120°
(e) 130°

34. LING is to FISH as
CARAVEL is to:

(a) MINSTREL
(b) CARAVAN
(c) CIRCUS
(d) VEHICLE
(e) BOAT

35. What is x?

$$\frac{4 \times 2 - 6}{7 - 4 \times 2} = x$$

36. Which word can be placed at the end of these words to make new words?

STIR
KIND
SAC   (_ _ _)
BAR
HAT

37. HIPPOPHOBIA is to HORSES as
AILUROPHOBIA is to:

(a) ELEPHANTS
(b) LIONS
(c) MICE
(d) SHARKS
(e) CATS

38. Complete the word.

_ _ U B R _ _ _ _

39. Which circle's letters cannot be rearranged into a six-letter word?

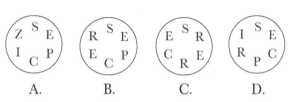

A.   B.   C.   D.

40. NECTAR is to DRINK as
AMBROSIA is to:

(a) MEDICINE
(b) BEES
(c) GREECE
(d) TONIC
(e) FOOD

1. What word should replace the question mark?

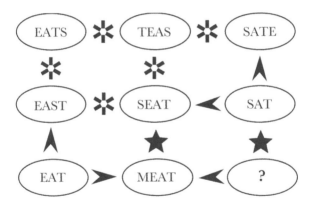

2. What do these words have in common?

AMULET, DEMURE, MORATORIUM, MULTIGERM

3. Consider the following square:

Now consider the following array:

Which square should replace the question mark?

A.   B.   C.   D.

4. "An adventurous action that runs counter to approved or conventional conduct." What word fits closest to this definition?

A. MISDEMEANOR;   B. ESCAPADE;
C. EXPERIENCE   D. VENTURE;
E. EXPLORATION

5. Move from star to star to spell out a ten-letter word.

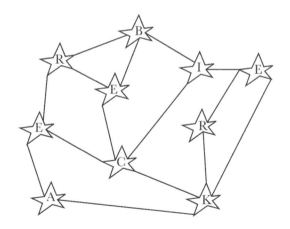

6. Sam visited several places in Europe.

He hated Madrid.
He loved Prague.
He hated Warsaw.
He hated Antrim.
He loved Ankara.

Did he love or hate Vienna?

7. Which number is the odd one out?

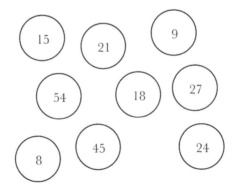

8. Find the starting point and visit each square once to reach the treasure marked T.

1S 1E	1S 1E	2S
1S	**T**	1N 2W
1E 2N	2N 1E	2W 1N

1N 2W
= 1 North
    2 West

9. Which is the odd one out?

ACETATE, NYLON, POLYESTER, VICUNA, RAYON

10. Solve each anagram to find two phrases that are spelled differently but sound alike. For example: A NAME, AN AIM.

IDLE LURES   ROSY DOLL

11. Insert two words that are anagrams of each other to complete the sentence. For example: She removed the <u>stain</u> from her new <u>satin</u> blouse.

Cheated out of what was rightfully mine, it would be a long, hard battle before I could _____ my inheritance. My solicitor warned me I could only hope for a _____, but I was determined to fight to the bitter end.

12. What number is three places away from itself plus 4, two places away from itself minus 3, three places from itself doubled, two places away from itself minus 1, three places away from itself plus 3, and two places away from itself minus 5?

19	14	3	8	11
9	2	20	6	5
15	22	16	2	30
24	7	18	4	10
18	1	12	13	17

13. What continues the below sequence?

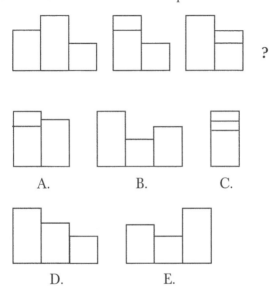

A.

B.

C.

D.

E.

14. Underline the two words in parentheses that the word outside the parentheses always has.

RIVER (ESTUARY, WATER, BOATS, MOVEMENT, WATERFALL)

15. Which is the missing section?

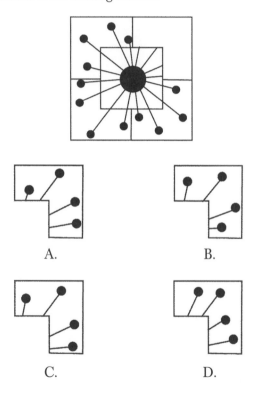

A.

B.

C.

D.

16. The cost of hiring a private rail carriage is shared equally by all the passengers. The carriage has seats for forty passengers and the total bill amounts to $70.37. How many passenger seats are not occupied?

17. What word is indicated from the clues below?

The bottom of the heap,
The end of the line,
The first of all,
The center of artichoke,
The beginning of the end.

18. What letter should replace the question mark?

19. Divide 800 by ¼ and add 5. What is the answer?

20. Rearrange the tiles so that every two adjacent letters form a word and two related words can be read around the outer edge.

Y Y A I	R S T O	E H M B
D E O M	T O A M	P F I B
O S T N	E S T A	O M A O

21.

is to ⟨ ⟩ as ◇ is to:

A.   B.   C.   D.

22. Place the letters in the grid to make a color and a lizard.

A A G H I K K N U I

23. What number comes next in the series?

0.5	(a) .857
0.666	(b) .861
0.75	(c) .865
0.8	(d) .869
0.833	(e) .873

24. What is the name given to a group of turtles?

(a) TRAIL
(b) SHELL
(c) KNOT
(d) WADDLE
(e) BALE
(f) NEST

25. Place three of the two-letter groups together to form a bird.

AN - IN - PI - DU - GE - NL

26. Simplify: $\dfrac{1}{3} \div \dfrac{7}{18}$

27. Which is the odd one out?

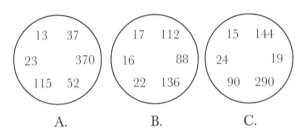

A.   B.   C.

28. There is an odd letter in each hexagon. Can you find them?

1.   2.   3.

29. Which of these is not a bird?

  (a) PUFFIN
  (b) SISKIN
  (c) CALABASH
  (d) MALLARD
  (e) MERLIN
  (f) GOSHAWK

30. Find a twelve-letter bird made up of two six-letter words.

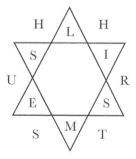

Six letters inside
Six letters outside

31. What symbol should continue the series?

?

32. By moving through the doorways spell out an eight-letter word.

33. Which word means the fear of travel?

(a) HODOPHOBIA
(b) NELOPHOBIA
(c) IDEOPHOBIA
(d) ANDROPHOBIA
(e) HYDROPHOBIA

34. Find three animals hidden in the following sentence:

"In the current times everyone will be a saver at least once with a pension."

35. How many degrees are there in this angle?

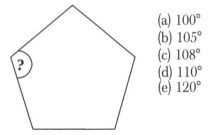

(a) 100°
(b) 105°
(c) 108°
(d) 110°
(e) 120°

36. What number should replace the question mark below?

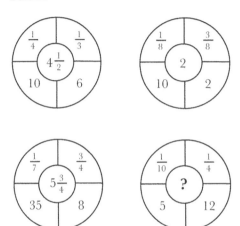

37. Fill in the missing letters to make a nine-letter word, starting from a corner square and continuing in a spiral to the center.

	E	I
I	D	N
A	R	

38. How many different teams of eleven players can be selected from fifteen members?

39. Fill in the missing letter to fit the rule of this pattern.

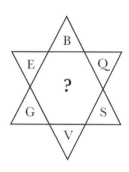

40. Change this fraction to a decimal.

$$\frac{3}{8} = ?$$

1. Complete the grid with the letters MAGIC so that no row, column, or diagonal line contains the same letter more than once.

	M			
A				
				G
			I	
		C		

2. I have correctly and accurately made a clear impact with the crown of a small fastener. What have I done?

3. If a car had increased its average speed for a 210-mile journey by 5 mph the journey would have been completed in 1 hour less. What was the original speed of the car for the journey?

4. Which is the odd one out?

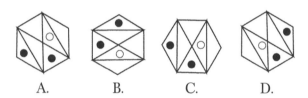

A.   B.   C.   D.

5. Add three consecutive letters of the alphabet to the group of letters below, without splitting the consecutive letters, to form another word.

DY

6. Which word is opposite in meaning to CORPULENT ?

OVERWROUGHT, COMMUNAL, HEALTHY, POOR, GAUNT

7. Which one of the following is not an anagram of LITTLE GIANT ENCYCLOPEDIA?

POLITICALLY DECENT EATING
ENTICED PATIENT LOGICALLY
IDENTICALLY ELECTING POET
ALLOCATED NICE TINY PIGLET
TANGENTIALLY CITED POLICE
DETECTING ALIAN OPTICALLY

8. JANUARY, MARCH, JUNE, OCTOBER, MARCH, ?

Which month comes next?

9. What letter should replace the question mark?

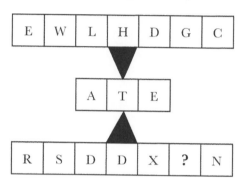

E	W	L	H	D	G	C

A	T	E

R	S	D	D	X	?	N

10. What number should replace the question mark?

9	4	6	11
3	6	7	4
5	?	4	1
11	6	3	8

11. Which circles should replace the ones with the question mark?

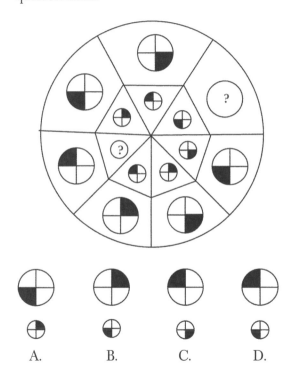

A.   B.   C.   D.

12. What number should replace the question mark in the circle?

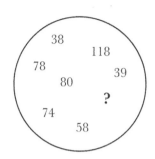

13. Seven synonyms of the keyword are shown. Take one letter from each of the seven synonyms in turn to spell out an eighth synonym of the keyword.

Keyword: TALENT
Synonyms: GIFT, ABILITY, KNACK, GENIUS, FLAIR, APTITUDE, CAPACITY

14. Following the rule of the sequence of numbers, what number should come next?

> 1, 4, 7, 11, 15, 13, 17, ?

15. REAR (LORRAINE) LION

What girl's name should go in the parentheses below according to the same rules as in the example above?

REIN (   ) AGOG

16. Four balls are placed in a row. The red ball is next to the green ball but not next to the blue ball. The yellow ball is not next to the blue ball. What ball is next to the yellow ball?

A. The red ball
B. The green ball
C. The red and the green ball
D. There is insufficient information to determine

17. One letter in each word of a well-known saying has been changed. What is the saying?

OLD ORE NUT

18. Which is the odd one out?

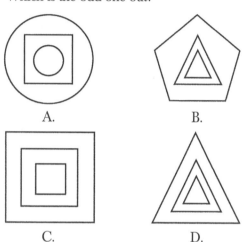

A.

B.

C.

D.

19. "An indirect, ingenious, and often cunning means to gain an end."

What word most closely fits the above definition?

PLAN, STRATAGEM, EXPEDIENCY, DIVERSION, FRAUD

20. Taking the respective numerical position of letters in the alphabet, decode the series of numbers in the box.

> 145144512191915814

For example: LITTLE GIANT = 1292020125791420

L	I	T	T	L	E	G	I	A	N	T
12	9	20	20	12	5	7	9	1	14	20

21. What number comes next in the series?

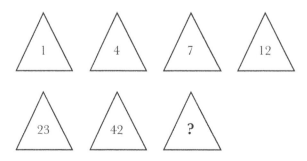

22. What number should replace the question mark?

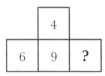

23. Find the missing word that will fit the rule of the below example.

ROPE (PART) ANTE

SHAM (_ _ _ _) PIER

24. If $3 \times 6 = 24$,
then $4 \times 3 = ?$

25. What is the missing number?

24	1	4	3
18	1	4	1
30	1	4	?

26. Starting at an outside square and moving in any direction, spell out a ten-letter name of a girl.

EG	NA	MO
AR	LD	RA
DE	BO	HI

27. A word can be placed in the parentheses that has the same meaning as the words outside. What is it? Each dash represents a letter.

STEAL (_ _ _ _ _) COOK IN WATER

28. The Beaufort wind scale is numbered from 0 to 17. Which number is storm?

(a) 8
(b) 9
(c) 10
(d) 11
(e) 12

29. Trace out a ten-letter word in any direction, using each letter once only.

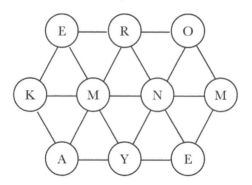

30. Place four of the three-letter groups together to make two six-letter words.

TTI - VIS - CAN - DER - ODI - MUR - OUS - SEC

31. What is the mathematical sign for arc of a circle?

(a) →
(b) ●
(c) ∪
(d) ⌒
(e) ▭

32. What number should replace the question mark?

1   12   3¼   10½   5½   9   7¾   ?

33. Complete the word.

_ _ _ G H C _ _ _

34. Simplify $\dfrac{675}{1000}$ as a fraction.

35. Fill in the blanks to find four girls' names.

A		N		E
E				I
E		I		A

36. Fill in the spaces to spell out these occupations.

```
_ I _ N _ L _ A _
_ O _ D _ L _ E _
_ A _ N _ Q _ I _
```

37. Complete the sequence.

38. Find the complete word that contains these middle letters. The word is hyphenated.

Z Z Y W

39. Which word will fit in front of these words to make new words?

(_ _ _)

HEAD
PRICK
STRIPE
BALL
CUSHION

40. With a standard six-sided die, how many throws are required on average before each of the six numbers has landed faceup?

(a) 10
(b) 15
(c) 20
(d) 25

1. Which four of the five pieces below can be used to construct a perfect circle?

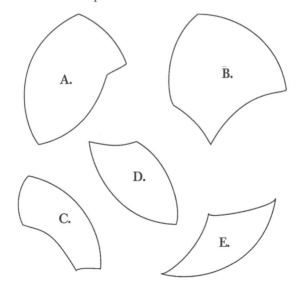

2. In which of the sentences below does the name of an animal *not* appear?

A. I was suddenly confronted by a group of evil-doers and hardened criminals.

B. Their leader appeared to be a swarthy, well-dressed Latin American wearing thick-rimmed, tinted spectacles.

C. "Who is this?" said a small, squat individual. "I don't trust him, he could be armed."

D. The leader roared with laughter and gesticulated with his bejewelled arm. "Believe me, he is quite harmless," he said. "But escort him from the premises immediately."

E. I walked out into the cold night air with a huge sigh of relief. This time I had avoided the trap easily, but I knew I might not be so lucky next time.

3. Which two of the following words are closest in meaning?

EXOTERIC, RECONDITE, PLAIN, DARK, REASONABLE, ROSEATE

4. What number should replace the question mark?

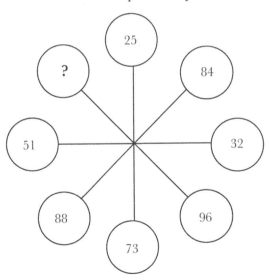

5. Arrange the letters in the squares below to find two nine-letter words that are antonyms.

	U	R	P	
V	D	R	T	O
S	R	E	S	P
Y	A	A		

6. What letter is immediately to the left of the letter two to the right of the letter four to the left of the letter two to the right of the letter C?

7. Which is the odd one out?

REAMER, GIMLET, CLEAVER, WIMBLE, AUGER

8. Which numbers should replace the question marks?

78	64	62	48	46	32
79	67	63	51	47	35
76	?	?	50	44	34
74	?	?	52	42	36
75	71	59	55	43	39
72	70	56	54	40	38

66	61
69	58

A.

66	61
68	56

B.

66	60
68	58

C.

64	61
69	56

D.

9. A well-known phrase has had all its vowels removed and has been split into groups of three letters. What is the phrase? All remaining letters are in the correct order.

HRT DYG NTM RRW

10. What do the following words have in common?

APPROPRIATE
BOW
DESERT
DOVE
ENTRANCE
GILL
LEAD
SLAVER

11. You have a range of weights available from 1 to 10. They are all single weights. Which one should you use to balance the scale and where should you place it?

12. is to as

 is to:

A.   B.   C.   D.

13.

  is to   as

  is to: **?**

A.	B.	C.	D.

14. Think of a four-letter word that reverses its meaning when the letter "T" is placed in front of it.

15. What letter should replace the question mark?

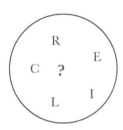

16. The following is extracted from what hyphenated word?

_ _ _ _ S – EX _ _ _ _ _ _ _ _ _

Clue: Third degree

17. SHORT LANCE is an anagram of which American city?

18. In a game of six players that lasts for 50 minutes, two reserves substitute for each player so that all players, including reserves, are on the pitch for the same length of time. How long is each player on the pitch?

19. What comes next in the below sequence?

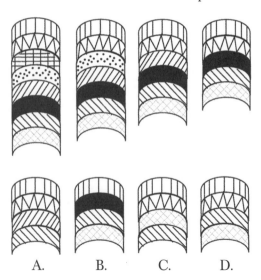

A.　　　B.　　　C.　　　D.

20. OVERUSED : CLICHÉD
OVERATTENTIVE :

CHINTZY, SCHOLASTIC, IRRITABLE,
IMPERIOUS, OFFICIOUS

21. What is the meaning of TULLE?

(a) VEGETABLE
(b) SILK FABRIC
(c) A MYSTIC
(d) TENSILE
(e) WEAPON

22. Fill in the blanks to find three minerals.

_ L _ M _ N _ M

_ A _ N _ S _ U _

_ A _ G _ N _ S _

23. Find a one-word anagram from the two words below.

DEEP DRESS

24. Which arrangement of pipes would carry most water?

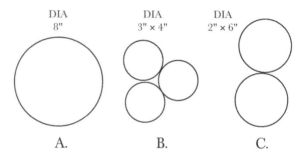

DIA
8"

DIA
3" × 4"

DIA
2" × 6"

A.

B.

C.

25. Which word continues this sequence?

SON, EAT, WORTH, ?

(A) REEL (B) LUNG (C) DEATH (D) PINE

26. Which are the odd ones out?

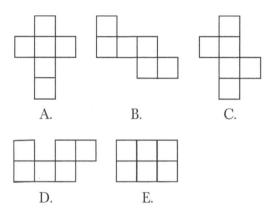

A.

B.

C.

D.

E.

27. Which of the following is always associated with SHERADISING?

(a) COPPER
(b) BRONZE
(c) ZINC
(d) LEAD
(e) SILVER

28. By moving through the doorways spell out an eight-letter word.

29. Make one word using all ten letters.

TRIBE COSTS

Clue: Pertaining to midwifery

30. If the missing letters in the circle below are correctly inserted they will form an eight-letter word. The word will not have to be read in a clockwise direction, but the letters are consecutive. What is the word and missing letters?

31. What number will replace the question mark?

28 47 85 ? 218 313 427

32. Place two of the three-letter groups together to form a food.

POT - MEL - CAR - SLI - OAT - WHE - MUE - ATE

33. What number should replace the question mark?

 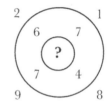

34. Find a three-letter word that completes all three words on the left-hand side and prefixes all three words on the right-hand side.

PAR		EYE
HAT	(_ _ _)	HOT
MAR		DEN

35. Fill in the missing letters to name a group of ducks.

_ A _ D _ I _ G

36. What is the opposite of PIETY?

(a) SOLACE
(b) HOLINESS
(c) GOODNESS
(d) IRREVERENCE
(e) PASSION

37. Find a twelve-letter fruit made up of two six-letter words.

One word inside
One word outside

38. The vowels have been omitted from this quotation. See if you can put them back in.

THFMLYTHTPRYSTGTHRSTYSTGTHR

39. What number should replace the question mark?

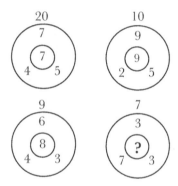

40. Place two of the three-letter groups together to make a six-letter vehicle.

OPY - SED - WAG - ONE - JAL - ANN

1. What comes next?

A.   B.   C.   D.

2. What number is missing from the left-hand circle?

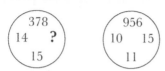

3. Add one letter, not necessarily the same letter, to each word at the front, end, or middle to find two words that are opposite in meaning.

SEND HARD

4. Pair the eight words below to form four longer words.

IRON, LOAD, FIRE, WORK, MAIN, GRID, WOOD, LAND

5. Find the number to replace the question mark.

369542 is to 246359
172896 is to 268179
417638 is to ?

6. What do these words have in common?

LIBERATION   CHINCHILLA
INITIALLY   SPEARMINT
FRAGRANCE   PERFUME
CLAUSTROPHOBIA

7. What letter should replace the question mark?

18		4		22
S		E		?
7		21		3

8. Insert the letters of the phrase AN AGENT'S GAMMA into the following once each only to complete a palindromic sentence, that is, one that reads the same backwards and forwards. For example, MADAM, I'M ADAM.

_ _ T _ _ _ _ ' _ _ _ _ E _ _ _

Clue: Doorkeeper's ID

9. DAWN is to DAY as
WINTER is to:

AUTUMN, SEASON, NIGHT, SPRING,
SUMMER

10. What phrase is indicated below?

11. What number should replace the question mark?

2	3	4	2
6	1	4	4
4	2	2	5
5	3	7	?

12. Solve the clues to find four six-letter words. The same three letters are represented by XYZ in each word.

XYZ _ _ _ Clue: Falls

_ XYZ _ _ Clue: Hangs fabric

_ _ XYZ _ Clue: Graze

_ _ _ XYZ Clue: Snare

13. Which two words that sound alike but are spelled differently mean: SOLITARY, ADVANCE?

14. What are the missing letters:

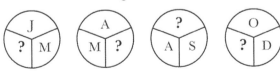

15. Fill in the missing word in the crossword below:

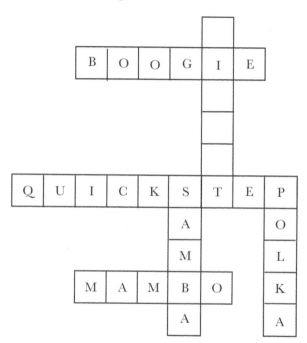

16. Which is the odd one out?

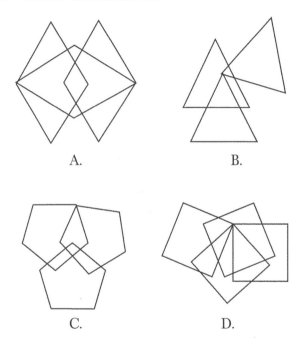

A.

B.

C.

D.

17. Fill in the consonants to complete four words that have the same meaning.

_ E _ E _ O U _

_ _ A _ I _ A _ L _

_ E _ E _ O _ E _ _

_ I _ _

Clue: Openhanded

18. Move from letter to letter horizontally and vertically, but not diagonally, to spell out a twelve-letter word. You have to find the starting point and provide the missing letters.

	M	M	E
R	I		N
I	S	O	

19. Which is the odd word out?

COMPRESS
DIMINISH
EBB
VANISH
DEPLETE

20. Place the letters in the grid to make a warm-blooded and a cold-blooded animal.

A A E K L L M S T

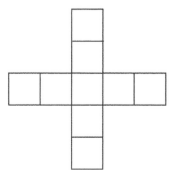

21. Which four-letter word placed inside the parentheses will complete these words?

(_ _ _ _) RAL   E (_ _ _ _) NT

22. Place two of the four-letter groups together to make a word.

TURN - EFUL - TACE - WACK - SPIT - INGS

23. Which word will carry on the sequence?

HALF-MAST, TAVERNER, RIPARIAN, NOBILITY, YULETIDE, ?

(a) DOUBLOON
(b) EXCITING
(c) MACARONI
(d) OVERTONE
(e) SKY PILOT
(f) TICKLISH

24. Find a six-letter word made up of only the following four letters.

AJ
MP

25. Change this fraction to a decimal.

$$\frac{7}{8} =$$

26. LEG is to FIBULA
as ARM is to:

(a) COCCYX
(b) THORAX
(c) CLAVICLE
(d) ULNA
(e) SCAPULA

27. Rearrange the two five-letter words to form a ten-letter word meaning "kind to strangers."

HABIT POLES

28. Which of the following is associated with HASLET?

(a) PATE
(b) BREAD
(c) ENTRAILS
(d) KIPPERS
(e) GINGER

29. Which word can be placed on the end of these words to make new words?

PILL
POT
GARB   (_ _ _)
FOOT
DAM

30. What is the symbol for CHROMIUM?

(a) C
(b) Ch
(c) Cr
(d) Cm
(e) Chm

31. Fill in the missing letters to name a group of cats.

_ L _ T _ E _

32. Fill in the missing letters to spell out different foods.

_ A _ B _ R _ E _

_ I _ C _ M _ A _

_ P _ G _ E _ T _

33. What does OROGRAPHY deal with?

(a) DESERTS
(b) TREES
(c) LAKES
(d) MOUNTAINS
(e) CAVES

34. Make up four pairs of words to find the odd one.

TOKEN	ICE	GREEN
SQUARE	SALTS	PEPPERS
FLOE	MAGIC	BATH

35. What is associated with GNOCCHI?

(a) SARDINES
(b) STRAWBERRIES
(c) MELONS
(d) TAPIOCA
(e) DUMPLINGS

36. To what does the adjective DIACONAL refer?

    (a) DIAMOND SHAPED
    (b) CONVERSATION
    (c) TEACHER
    (d) DEACON
    (e) WEALTH

37. DELTIOLOGY is the study of

    (a) RIVER MOUTHS
    (b) PICTURE POSTCARDS
    (c) BRIDGES
    (d) PRISONS
    (e) FINGERS

38. One man can mow a lawn in 6 hours, and another man can mow the same lawn in 3 hours. If they both worked together at their respective rates, how long would they take?

39. PISSIFORM is to PEA SHAPED as
CLAVIFORM is to:

(a) CROSS SHAPED
(b) WEB SHAPED
(c) CLUB SHAPED
(d) SQUARE SHAPED
(e) SWORD SHAPED

40. What number should replace the question mark?

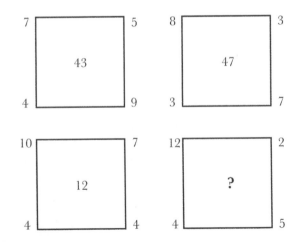

1. Divide the square into four equal sections so that each section contains the same three symbols twice.

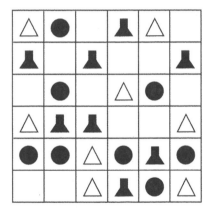

2. Take one letter from each circle and, reading clockwise, spell out an eight-letter word meaning "escort." You have to find the starting point.

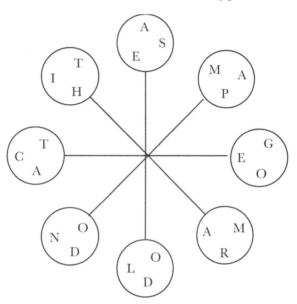

3. What number comes next in this sequence?

0, 0, 1, 3, 6, 6, 7, 9, 12, 12, 13, ?

4. Arrange the words into the correct order and say whether the resulting statement is true or false.

LOVE WAS CUPID GREEK THE OF GOD

5. How many minutes before 10 AM is it if 90 minutes later it will be as many minutes after 11 AM?

6. Seven synonyms of the keyword are shown. Take one letter from each of the synonyms to spell out an eighth synonym of the keyword.

Keyword: METHOD

Synonyms: FORM, MANNER, COURSE, SCHEME, ROUTINE, MODE, PLAN

7. Insert the name of an American city into the bottom line to complete the three-letter words.

N	A	M	O	T	S	C	W	B
I	C	I	B	A	A	A	O	A

8. If 9L of a C is 9 lives of a cat, can you decode the following?

90D in a R.A.

9. How many more circles of the same size as the one already placed below will completely cover the square?

10. Create two words using each of the ten letters only once:

HIRBOMEDPA

Clue: Macabre mountain

11. Insert the letters provided into each quadrant to form two words that form a noun, one reading clockwise around the inner circle and one counterclockwise around the outer circle.

NE: FNOK
SE: NINI
SW: DTGA
NW: RUIN

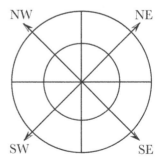

12. Fill in the missing numbers.

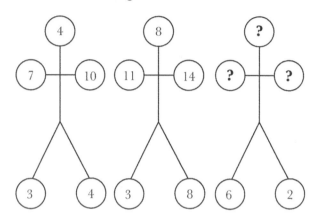

13. Start at a corner letter and spiral clockwise around the perimeter squares to spell out a nine-letter word that ends at the center square. You have to provide the missing letters.

C		I
S	M	T
I		I

14. What do these words have in common?

GLIMMER, CHORTLE, MOTEL, FLOUNDER

15. Which option below continues the below sequence?

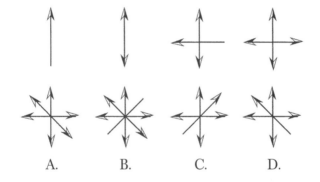

A. B. C. D.

16. Place two four-letter groups together to make an eight-letter word that is a bone in the body.

ICLE - LLAN - PATE - SPHE - ILAC - CLAV

17. What number is two places away from itself plus 2, one place away from itself plus 5, two places away from itself less 3, and two places away from itself plus 1?

4	16	9	10
15	2	13	5
7	12	8	14
6	1	3	11

18. From these three words, find the two words that will form an anagram that is a synonym of the word remaining.

For example: LEG – MEEK – NET = MEEK – GENTLE (LEG – NET)

GAP – GALA – NEAT

19. What well-known phrase is indicated below?

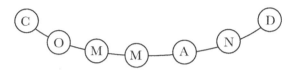

20. Solve the cryptogram below. Each letter of the alphabet has been substituted by another.

KCSSAKK PK HAUUPBH NXDU FIC
NDBU. XDGGPBAKK PK TPZPBH
NXDU FIC HAU. —X. EDSZKIB LJINB

21. Place a word in the parentheses that when placed at the end of the first word makes a word and when placed in front of the second word also makes a word.

OPERA (_ _ _) US

22. Insert each of the letters of the phrase STAB DERRIERE into the grid only once to find two related words.

Clue: Strike it rich!

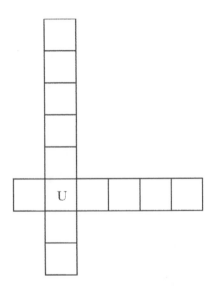

23. What is the meaning of GIGA?

    (a) 10^5
    (b) 10^6
    (c) 10^7
    (d) 10^8
    (e) 10^9

24. What type of animal is an ORYX?

    (a) ANTELOPE
    (b) MONKEY
    (c) LLAMA
    (d) RAT
    (e) SHEEP

25. Place three of the two-letter groups together to form a tree.

SE - NK - SP - GO - GI - RU

26. Use each pair of letters once to form four four-letter vegetables—one pair is not used.

27. Which of these is not an anagram of a dog?

(a) UAUACHHHI
(b) LLOPAPIN
(c) SNACHON
(d) HDNEKLOU
(e) LAUSKI
(f) GIROC

28. Find three birds hidden in this passage: "After the storm then we must fly the balloon at once; it will be awful."

29. If the missing letters in the two circles below are correctly inserted, they will form synonymous words. The words do not have to be read in a clockwise direction, but the letters are consecutive. What are the words and missing letters?

 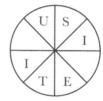

30. What is always part of a DEMIJOHN?

(a) GREAT AGE
(b) GOLD CAP
(c) SQUARE BODY
(d) NARROW NECK
(e) BLUE LABEL

31. How many triangles are there in this figure?

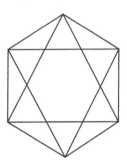

32. What number should replace the question mark?

Simplify: $8 - 6 \times 7 - 10 \div 5 + 1 = ?$

33. Which two words have opposite meanings?

DISORDER, IMMODEST, HEEDFUL,
INFUSION, OBLIVIOUS, INNATE

34. Which circle's letters cannot be rearranged into a six-letter word?

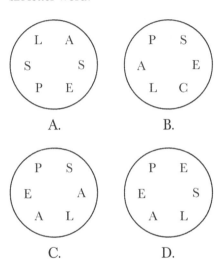

A.

B.

C.

D.

35. What number should continue the series?

4 7 9 8 7 5 6 9 5 7 5 ?

36. Find a seven-letter word by moving along the
lines connecting the circles.

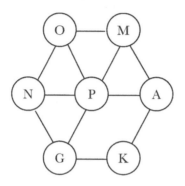

37. What word will fit in front of these words to
make new words?

$$(\ \_\_\_\ )$$

COAT
KNOT
HEAVY
SAIL
HAT

38. Find a twelve-letter
animal made up of
two six-letter words—
one word inside, one
word outside.

39. What number should replace the question mark?

219   208   186   ?   109   54   –12

40. Which word means the same as CHAGRIN?

(a) IDLENESS
(b) SMILING
(c) ANNOYANCE
(d) BENEFIT
(e) PENSIVE

1. What number
should replace
the question
mark?

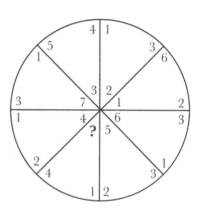

2. "The ability to exert effort for a purpose." What
word below best fits this definition?

CAPABILITY, POTENTIAL, VIGOR,
TALENT, POWER

3. Find a four-letter word that forms a different
word with each preceding letter or letters.

C
L
SH
DR
H   (_ _ _ _)
R
CL
PL
M

4. What letter is missing from the pyramid?

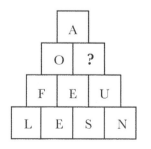

5. Insert each of the letters in the phrase ESOTERIC DEVISE into the grid once to find two connected words.

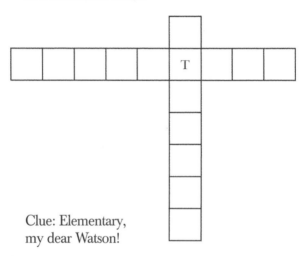

Clue: Elementary, my dear Watson!

6. Simplify to find x:

$$\frac{-7 \times 3 \times 2}{3 \times 2 \times 7} = x$$

7. Which hexagon should replace the question mark?

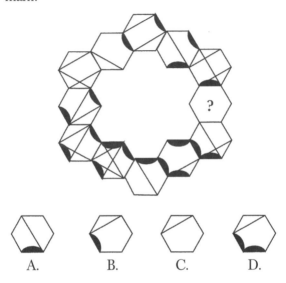

A. B. C. D.

8. Which two words are opposite in meaning?

FLAT, CONCAVE, REVERSED, STRAIGHT, BULGING, EMPTY

9. Solve the three anagrams to produce a well-known quotation by Sir John Vanbrugh.

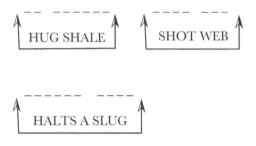

10. Choose a word from the right-hand column to accompany the words in the left-hand column.

INOPPORTUNE		AGLOW
DEFEAT		FIRST
ASTUTE		RIDDEN
CALMNESS		PLEASE
?		REMOTE

11. What number should replace the question mark?

	1	
3		5
7		5

	2	
1		2
4		6

	3	
?		3
7		3

12. What is the value of the second line?

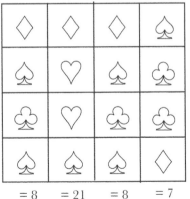

13. Find the starting point and track from letter to letter along the lines to spell out the name of an American river (eleven letters).

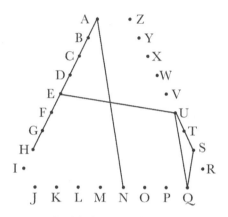

There is one double-letter in the name.

14. A familiar phrase has been split up and jumbled into three-letter groups. Find the saying. For example, FIND THE QUOTE could be jumbled up into DTH, OTE, FIN, EQU.

OPO, EWO, FTH, ONT, RLD

15. Each number has a choice of three letters.
Dial an American writer (8, 5):
32676722 77235

16. Take a letter from each tree in turn to spell out five types of tree.

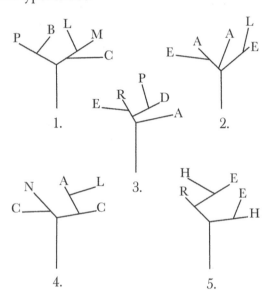

1.

2.

3.

4.

5.

17. Simplify: $\dfrac{1}{4} \div \dfrac{7}{8}$

18. What numbers should appear on the bottom row?

15	13	19	22
37	34	35	32
69	72	66	69
?	?	?	?

19. Which number is the odd one out?

20. Insert a word that completes the first word and starts the second.

DO (_ _ _) NECK

21. Complete the words to form names of animals. Then rearrange the initial letters of each word to find a sixth animal.

_ L _ N _

_ E _ N _ E _ R

_ E _ U

_ N _ E _ O _ E

_ U _ F _ L _

22. What is associated with DANCETTE?

(a) CIRCUS
(b) PUPPET
(c) CAROUSEL
(d) STATUE
(e) ZIGZAG

23. A company asked its workforce to increase production by 6% per week. If the employees worked a 5-day week, how much more would they need to produce each day to achieve the desired 6% weekly increase?

24. Make one word using all ten letters.

SCOOP CRIME

Clue: Scientific instrument

25. What is the name given to a group of WILD-FOWL?

(a) PLUMP
(b) CLAMOUR
(c) CLUSTER
(d) WING
(e) CHATTERING
(f) BLAST

26. By moving through the doorways spell out an eight-letter word.

27. Fill in the blanks to find three boats.

_ E _ T _ O _ E _

_ I _ E _ A _ E _

_ R _ O _ S _ I _

28. Find the eight-letter word.

1 2 3 4) HOLE - PAIN (5 6 7 8

6 5 1 4) _ _ _ _ _ _ _ _ (3 7 2 8

29. What number should replace the question mark?

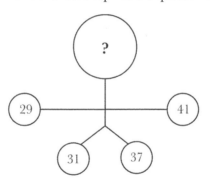

30. The library was selling off old books.

I purchased 12 for $12.
Some were 50¢, some were $1.50, some were $2.
How many of each did I buy?

31. How many degrees are there in this angle?

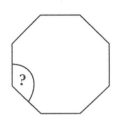

(a) 115°
(b) 120°
(c) 125°
(d) 130°
(e) 135°

32. Which is the odd one out?

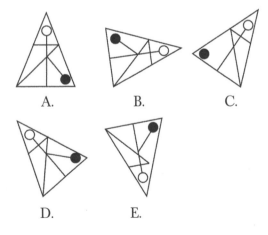

A. B. C.

D. E.

33. Which religious sign is the Greek cross?

(a) +
(b) T
(c) +
(d) ×
(e) +

34. Which word means the fear of FOOD?

(a) ARETEPHOBIA
(b) EOSOPHOBIA
(c) SITOPHOBIA
(d) GENOPHOBIA
(e) KINESOPHOBIA

35. "How heavy is this bag of rice?" I asked the shopkeeper.
"128 lbs divided by half its weight," he said.
How much did it weigh?

36. Place two of the three-letter groups together to form a tree.

LEA - UCE - CHI - ELA - SPR - LEN - PIN - BEE

37. Which temperature below is 68° Fahrenheit changed to Celsius?

(a) 18°C
(b) 19°C
(c) 20°C
(d) 21°C
(e) 22°C

38. What is the meaning of ARGOT?

(a) SILVER
(b) NUBILE
(c) GOLD INGOT
(d) GOODS
(e) SLANG

39. Trace out a ten-letter word in any direction, using each letter once only.

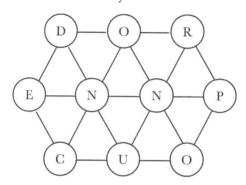

40. In how many different ways can the Olympic rings be arranged in color order?

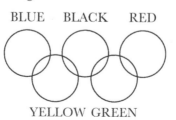

BLUE   BLACK   RED

YELLOW GREEN

1. If meat in a river (3 in 6) is T(HAM)ES, can you find frozen rain in a country (4 in 8)?

2. Insert the missing consonants to complete a magic square where all words read the same across and down.

		A		E
	I		E	
A		I		I
	E		I	
E		I		

B, L, D, G, S,
D, D, R, L, R,
B, T, D, T

3. You are looking for one word in this paragraph. The word appears only once, its first letter being the eighth letter after a certain vowel. The same vowel is the tenth letter to appear after its last letter. What is the word?

4. What number is missing from the third hexagon?

5. Which is the odd one out?

PATELLA, FIBULA, RADIUS, FEMUR, TIBIA

6. TANS = 8
CAVE = 9
LEAF = 12
TAX = ?

7. Change FIRE to WATER. The asterisks in each word are common to the word above it.

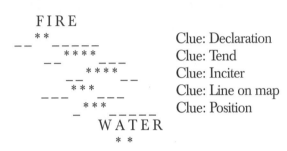

FIRE

* *
_ _   _ _ _ _ _
   * * * *
   _ _   _ _ _
     * * * *
     _ _   _ _
   * * *
  _ _ _   _ _ _
    * * *
   _   _ _ _ _ _

WATER

* *

Clue: Declaration
Clue: Tend
Clue: Inciter
Clue: Line on map
Clue: Position

8. What number should replace the question mark?

225 | ?
150 | 335
555 | 410
520 | 445

9. Which comes next?

?

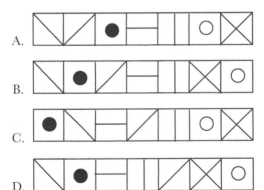

10. Complete the three hyphenated words:

_ _ _ _ T – H _ _ E – B _ _ _ _

Clue: Lack of success

11. Which figure continues the below sequence?

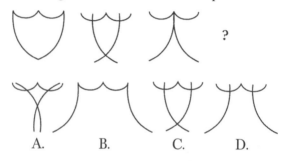

12. Eliminate twelve letters from the phrase below to leave a word meaning "shakes."

READ BETWEEN THE LINES

13. POST- : LATER

MACRO- :
> LATE
> LANGUAGE
> SMALL
> LARGE
> LAST

14. Solve the cryptic clue below. The answer is a thirteen-letter anagram contained within the clue.

> NURSE I SPY
> GYPSIES RUN
> WHEN I'M
> ON RAPID
> CALL.

15. What number should replace the question mark?

Simplify: $6 - 3 \times 2 + 8 \div 4 + 6 = ?$

16. What number should replace the question mark?

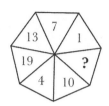

17. Which is the odd one out?

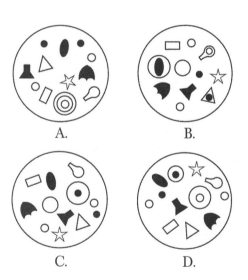

A.

B.

C.

D.

18. Place two letters in each pair of parentheses so that they finish the word on the left and start the word on the right. Reading downwards, combine these pairs to spell out a six-letter musical word.

LE (_ _) D

WI (_ _) IN

G (_ _) IT

19. A train traveling at a speed of 40 mph enters a tunnel that is $1\frac{1}{4}$ miles long. The length of the train is $\frac{1}{4}$ mile. How long does it take for all of the train to pass through the tunnel, from the moment the front enters to the moment the rear emerges?

20. Simplify $\frac{175}{1000}$ as a fraction.

21. BEDROOMS, ROMANTIC, ANSWERED, WEAKENED, ?

Which is the next word?

KEYBOARD, ABDICATE, CATACOMB, KILOBYTE

22. Which is the odd one out?

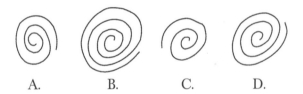

A.   B.   C.   D.

23. What is the product of the largest prime number multiplied by the smallest even number?

8	41	83
53	10	67
71	11	6

24. GAGGLE is to GEESE
as POD is to

(a) FLAMINGOS
(b) CROCODILES
(c) BEARS
(d) WHALES
(e) SPIDERS

25. What is the meaning of FAUCET?

(a) HAT
(b) TAP
(c) MASK
(d) FOUNTAIN
(e) DOCK

26. Find a six-letter word made up of only the following four letters.

OM
IN

27. DANCER is to RHUMBA
as SINGER is to

(a) BASSOON
(b) POLKA
(c) COULOMB
(d) DOTTEREL
(e) MADRIGAL

28. Place four of the three-letter groups together to make two six-letter words.

ATO - PIN - WRE - ILE - SEN - ATH - NSH - DON

29. Place a word in the parentheses that when placed on the end of the first word makes a word and when placed in front of the second word also makes a word.

DESSERT (_ _ _ _ _) BILL

30. Fill in the blanks to find words to do with building.

A		T		C
S				Y
E		E		T

31. Complete word that contains these middle letters.

_ _ _ NGIP _ _ _

32. Find a one-word anagram from the two words below.

SANE DOSE

33. What is the mathematical sign for summation?

(a) Π
(b) Σ
(c) ≈
(d) ¤
(e) ◊

34. Which two words are similar in meaning?

AWKWARD, BRISK, GAMIN, TEAM,
SPORTSMAN, URCHIN

35. Place the letters in the grid to
make a shell and a weapon.

A C C C E
H L N O

36. What is the opposite of ESPOUSE?

    (a) OPPOSE
    (b) WELCOME
    (c) DISMAY
    (d) HUSBAND
    (e) INFORM

37. Complete the sequence.

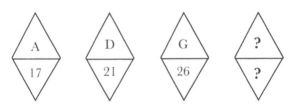

38. Fill in the missing letters to complete the word.

    _ _ _ CHW _ _ _

39. Which word can be placed on the end of these words to make new words?

WAS
WIT
ZIT
FAT
GAT

$(\_\,\_\,\_)$

40. Rearrange the two five-letter words to form a ten-letter word meaning "type of shellfish."

PART GOODS

1. Solve the anagram in parentheses to complete the quotation correctly.

(Gain into arm) is the eye of the soul. —Joubert

2. Which line of figures is the odd one out?

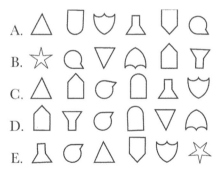

3. What phrase is indicated here?

4. 59 is to 98 as 65 is to

$$59, \ 86, \ 89, \ 56$$

5. Add one letter, not necessarily the same letter, to each word in the front, end, or middle to find two words that are opposite in meaning.

ALLY, ROSE

6. Some widgets are brown. Everything brown has a straight edge. Therefore, which of the following must be true?

A. All widgets have a straight edge.
B. Everything brown is a widget.
C. Some widgets have a straight edge.

7. What number should replace the question mark?

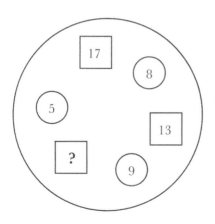

8. Find three words starting with the letters OPP
that are opposite in meaning to the words given:

A. LIBERATE = OPP _ _ _ _
B. CONCURRENCE = OPP _ _ _ _ _ _ _
C. UNTIMELY = OPP _ _ _ _ _ _

9. Read clockwise to find a
ten-letter word. You
must find the starting
point and provide the
missing letters. The
word you are looking
for starts and finishes
with the same two letters.

10. Alter one letter in each of the words below to
form four new words of the same theme.

BALL, HARM, CUTE, FINE

11. Which is the missing section?

A.

B.

C.

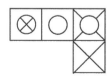

D.

12. What number should replace the question mark?

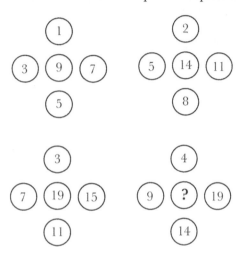

13. Which word is closest in meaning to FRETFUL?

GUILTY, PETULANT, UNNERVED,
DISMAYED, FRANTIC

14. Insert each of the letters of the phrase ELFIN LENSES once in the spaces below to complete a palindromic sentence—that is, one that reads the same backwards and forwards. For example, MADAM, I'M ADAM.

_ _ _ I _ _ _ _ _ _ _ E _

Clue: Old toms

15. How many lines appear below?

16. Find the complete word that contains these middle letters. The word is hyphenated.

_ _ PPLEG _ _ _

17. Find five words starting at the top of the pyramid and taking one letter from each row in turn. Every letter in the pyramid is used at least once.

18. Match each word in column A with a related word in column B.

A	B
SHEET	TURN
LAPEL	WRITE
NUT	WRAP
PAPER	CRACK

19. What is the missing section?

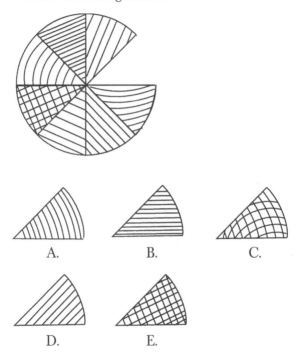

A. B. C.

D. E.

20. In a horse race the first five places were filled by Horses 3, 7, 18, 9, and 16. The jockey of Horse 3 wore a crimson shirt, the jockey of Horse 7 wore green, jockey 18 wore red, and 9 wore ivory. What color did the jockey of Horse 16 wear? Was it yellow, purple, black, or maroon?

21. Insert the name of a tree into the bottom line to complete the three-letter words.

H	S	P	P	T	A	S	T
E	P	E	I	O	I	K	E

22. What number should replace the question mark?

27   28½   31½   ?   42   49½   58½

23. If the missing letters in the circle below are correctly inserted they will form an eight-letter word. The word does not have to be read in a clockwise direction, but the letters are consecutive. What is the word and missing letters?

24. What number in the decimal system is represented by this binary notation?

1100110   (a) 56
               (b) 98
               (c) 100
               (d) 102
               (e) 104

25. What is a slice across a cone that is not parallel to, or does not pass through, the base called?

(a) CYCLOID
(b) HYPERBOLA
(c) PARABOLA
(d) ELLIPSE

26. Which mathematical symbol should replace the question mark to continue the series?

× − + ÷ × − + ÷ × ?

27. Place a word in the parentheses that when placed on the end of the first word makes a word, and when placed in front of the second word also makes a word.

SAND (_ _ _) GAIN

28. This is a treasure map. The treasure is marked T. You have to find the starting square. 2N means move 2 squares north.

N

T	1E	2S	3W
3E	1S	1W	2S
1S	2E	2W	2N
2E	3N	2N	2W

W (left)   E (right)

S

29. If 6 × 4 = 26,
then 5 × 4 = ?

30. What number replaces the question mark?

15   1   10¾   3⅛   6½   5¼   ?

31. What is the name given to a group of SNIPE?

(a) GATHERING
(b) SPRING
(c) TUFT
(d) STALK
(e) GAME
(f) WISP

32. Place two of the four-letter groups together to make a word.

RBID - VIRT - WHAC - UNDE - UOSA - INGS

33. Which of these is not a fruit?

(a) KUMQUAT
(b) ANANAS
(c) PEARMAIN
(d) TAMARIND
(e) MUSCATEL
(f) EPHEMERA

34. Find the three fish hidden in this sentence:
"When you have played the red ace, change
limits to perhaps one pound per point."

35. Rearrange the letters to form two seven-letter
words that are synonyms. Each word commences
with the center letter.

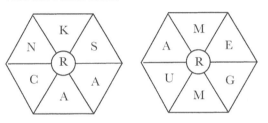

36. Which temperature below is 15° Celsius changed
to Fahrenheit?

(a) 58°F
(b) 59°F
(c) 60°F
(d) 61°F
(e) 62°F

37. The vowels have been omitted from this quotation. See if you can insert them back in.

WNNGSNTVRYTHNGTSTHNLYTHNG

38. Make one word using all ten letters.

STRIDE CHAP

Clue: Sender

39. Find a twelve-letter insect made of two six-letter words, one word inside, one word outside.

40. Starting at an outside square and moving in any direction, spell out the name of a ten-letter continent.

DA	CA	AN
TI	MB	TA
OD	RC	IA

TEST 13

1. Six antonyms of the keyword are shown. Take one letter from each of the six antonyms to spell out a seventh antonym of the keyword.

Keyword: OUTSET

Antonyms: FINISH, CLOSING, END, TERMI-NATION, CONCLUSION, COMPLETION

2. Which is the odd pair of letters?

BY, HS, EV, JR, GT

3. Insert a word that finishes the first word and starts the second.

DAM		ANT

4. What comes next in the below sequence?

?

5. Take one letter from each circle and, reading clockwise, spell out an eight-letter word meaning "solemn." You have to find the starting point.

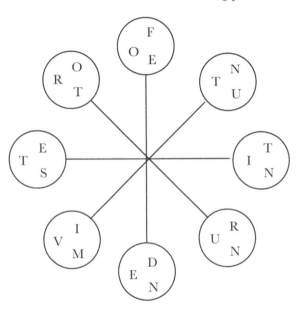

6. Fill in the missing letters to complete the word below:

_ I _ I _ I _ I _ I _ Y

Clue: Shares

7. What number should replace the question mark?

2	6	3	3	8	5
9	5	6	2	9	7
4	6	1	6	9	2
2	1	9	7	5	8
7	9	1	2	9	6
4	1	7	8	?	3

8. Take one word from each column to make four compound words. For example: the five words DOOR, STEP, SON, NET, WORK would produce the words: DOORSTEP, STEPSON, SONNET, NETWORK.

A	B	C	D	E
PORT	SOME	ON	HOPE	BORN
FEAR	TIME	DUMB	EVER	MORE
PART	LESS	MOON	NEW	FREE
SING	ABLE	WHERE	STRUCK	GREEN
OVER	LET	SHARE	COST	LESS

9. Rearrange the two five-letter words to find a ten-letter word meaning "two-masted vessel."

BRAIN TINGE

10. What continues the sequence?

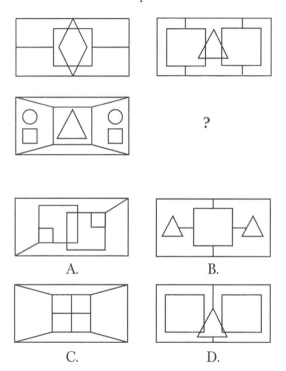

?

A.

B.

C.

D.

11. All the following words relate to meetings:
CAUCUS, AUDIENCE, ENCOUNTER,
FORUM, RALLY, SEMINAR, SYNOD,
SUMMIT, CONFERENCE.

Match each of the words with its correct
definition below:

i) Casual and unplanned
ii) Discussion of a specialized academic theme
iii) Public discussion
iv) Local political party to decide policy
v) Conference between heads of government
vi) Exchange of views or securing advice
vii) Formal meeting with VIP
viii) Public assembly for a political cause
ix) Meeting or council of church officials

12. "To consider or examine attentively or deliberately."
Which word below does *not* fit this definition?

MEDIATE, PONDER, RUMINATE,
REFLECT, DELIBERATE

13. Make PIE HUMBLE by following these instructions:

      PIE

1. Change a letter: _ _ _
2. Change a letter: _ _ _
3. Change a letter: _ _ _
4. Add three letters: HUMBLE

14. What famous European landmark is indicated here?

R	F	A
A	A	R
G	L	T

15. What word can be placed on the end of these words to make new words?

CHIN
BLAME
PAIN   (_ _ _ _)
COLOR
HARM

16. Move from star to star to spell out a ten-letter phrase (2, 2, 1, 5).

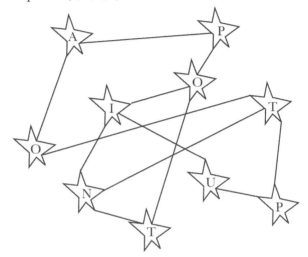

17. BADGER (ABIDE) PIERCE

Using the same rules as the above example, what word should appear in the parentheses below?

NECTAR (_ _ _ _ _) CARPET

18.

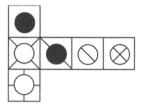

When the above is folded to form a cube, just one of the following can be produced. Which one?

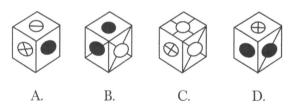

A.   B.   C.   D.

19. Make up four pairs of words and find the odd one.

CRAZY	MEATY	POST
APPLE	FIRST	TURNOVER
SEAS	GANG	CHINA

20. Insert the missing word in the crossword below:

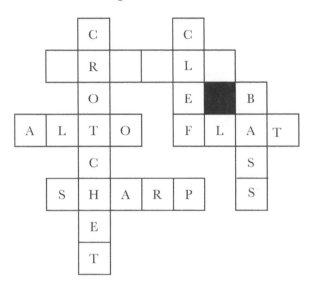

21. Simplify $\dfrac{925}{1000}$ as a fraction.

22. Find the missing square.

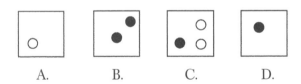

| A. | B. | C. | D. |

23. 3 apples + 4 bananas cost 29¢, and 1 apple + 8 bananas cost 43¢. How much is 1 banana?

24. How many minutes is it before 12:00 noon if 70 minutes ago it was four times as many minutes past 9:00 AM?

25. Complete the five words so that two letters are common to each word—i.e., the same two letters that end the first word also start the second word, and so on. The two letters that end the fifth word are the first two letters of the first word, thus completing the association.

```
_ _ N A _ _
_ _ D I _ _
_ _ P I _ _
_ _ C E _ _
_ _ B T _ _
```

26. Rearrange the letters to find two seven-letter words that are synonyms. Each word commences with the central letter.

 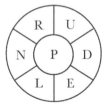

27. Which figure below carries on the sequence?

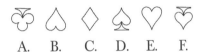
A. B. C. D. E. F.

28. Change this fraction to a decimal: $\frac{1}{16}$.

29. Fill in the missing letters to make a nine-letter word, starting from a corner square and continuing in a spiral to the center.

F		O
U	E	T
	C	A

30. Place three of the two-letter groups together to form a card game.

PO - PI - RI - ET - KE - QU

31. Which two words have opposite meanings?

VIVACIOUS, INDIFFERENCE,
TRIBULATION, HAPPINESS,
SARCASM, DISTRACTION

32. If the missing letters in the two circles below are correctly inserted they will form synonymous words. The words do not have to be read in a clockwise direction, but the letters are consecutive. What are the words and missing letters?

33. Which of the following is always associated with FLAVIN?

(a) YELLOW
(b) BLUE
(c) PINK
(d) MAUVE
(e) WHITE

34. Fill in the blanks to form different sports.

_ A _ M _ N _ O _
_ R _ S _ L _ N _
_ I _ L _ A _ D _

35. What number should replace the question mark?

Simplify: 10 + 12 ÷ 4 + 2 × 9 − 10 = ?

36. Which two words are similar in meaning?

STRAINED, VERBOSE, BASIC, DULCET, DISPOSES, SWEET

37. Which word means the fear of dogs?

(a) KOPOPHOBIA
(b) PYROPHOBIA
(c) LALIOPHOBIA
(d) STASIPHOBIA
(e) CYNOPHOBIA

38. Find the three words that have these countries in them: WALES, CHAD, ITALY

```
_ W A _ _ L E S
_ _ C H A _ D
_ _ I T _ A L _ Y
```

39. Moving through the doorways spell out an eight-letter word.

40. What is the meaning of IDEOLOGY?

(a) IDOLATRY
(b) TRADE
(c) BELIEFS
(d) IDEALS
(e) COMMERCE

1.   ?

What continues the above sequence?

A.   B.   C.   D.

2. What term is indicated below?

_ _ A V I _ _

3. What letter is missing from the wall?

H	N	E		E
R		T	E	O
T	M		O	O
D	R	A	R	Y
O	G	W		?

4. What number should replace the question mark?

  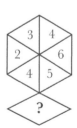

5. Which two words are the odd ones out?

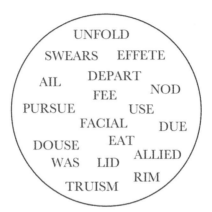

UNFOLD

SWEARS   EFFETE

AIL   DEPART

FEE   NOD

PURSUE   USE

FACIAL   DUE

DOUSE   EAT

WAS   LID   ALLIED

TRUISM   RIM

6. Arrange the words into the correct order, then say whether the resulting statement is true or false.

KNOWN ETRUSCANS ANCIENT CEN-TRAL THE AREA NOW CALLED THE INHABITANTS IN TUSCANY WERE AS OF ITALY

7. Which is the missing section?

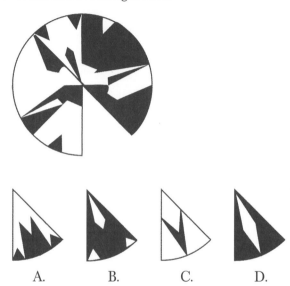

A.   B.   C.   D.

8. A car travels 20 miles in the same time as another car, traveling 20 mph faster, covers 30 miles. How long does the journey take?

9. Find the starting point and track from letter to letter along the lines to spell out a sixteen-letter phrase (8-3-5).

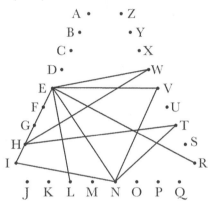

There are two sets of double letters in the phrase, including one that ends a word and starts the next.

10. Place two of the three-letter groups together to form an animal.

TIG - HOR - SEL - SEN - SHE - WEA - ERA - EPA

11. Each number has a choice of three letters.
Dial an explorer (5, 8):
65142 15752725

12. What number should replace the question mark?

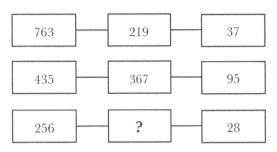

13. Arrange these words into four groups with each group containing three related words.

ASIDE, WISE, BACK, ZONE, DISC, MINE, BOMB, WORK, SAIL, TOWER, SCALE, RUSH

Clue: Set time on gold clock

14. On a shopping spree at Macy's, my wife spent half the money in her purse within 15 minutes. This meant she was left with as many cents as she had dollars before, and half as many dollars as she had cents before. How much money did she originally have?

15. Find the starting point and visit every square to reach the treasure marked T.

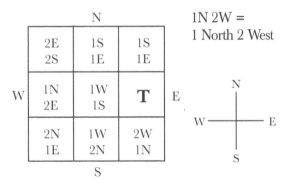

1N 2W =
1 North 2 West

16. Which is the missing square?

A.   B.   C.

17. What number should replace the question mark?

2   12 $5\frac{1}{4}$ $9\frac{3}{4}$ $8\frac{1}{2}$ $7\frac{1}{2}$?

18. Insert two words that are anagrams of each other to complete the sentence. For example: She removed the *stain* from her new *satin* dress.

A _____ fisherman, he knew exactly the right spot on the riverbank for some rich pickings. Sure enough, within a few moments he had on his face a look of pure satisfaction as the fish began to _____ into his net.

19. In the arrangement of numbers below, what is the difference between the sum of the two highest prime numbers and the produce of the two lowest square numbers?

8	23	3	49
19	4	29	17
37	25	35	16

20. Only ten letters of the alphabet do not appear in this grid. What ten-letter phrase can these ten letters be used to spell out?

J	Q	F	B
O	Z	K	G
N	W	Y	M
X	H	L	V

Clue: Slapstick

21. TURQUOISE : BLUE

JASPER :

        YELLOW
        RED
        ORANGE
        BROWN
        GREEN

22. A well-known phrase has had all its vowels removed and has been split into groups of three letters. What is the phrase? All remaining letters are in the correct order.

MTL DMR TNS CTY

23. Which is the odd one out?

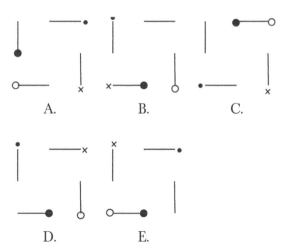

A. B. C.

D. E.

24. Unravel the logic behind this diagram to find which symbol should go into the square with the question mark.

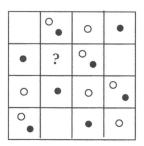

25. What word will fit in front of these words to form new words?

(_ _ _ _ _)

HEART
BREAD
TOOTH
WILLIAM
NESS

26. Find the eight-letter word.

1234) DINE – COMA (5678

5674) _ _ _ _ _ _ _ _ (1283

27. What number should replace the question mark?

28. What is struck when a glockenspiel is played?

(a) BARS
(b) STRINGS
(c) PIANO
(d) CYMBALS
(e) DRUMS

29. A word can be placed in the parentheses that has the same meaning as the words outside. What is it? Each dash represents a letter.

THIN METAL (_ _ _ _) THWART

30. What is the mathematical sign for square root?

(a) $\neq$
(b) $\square$
(c) f
(d) $\sqrt{}$
(e) $''$

31. Which word means the same as MAWKISH?

(a) UGLY
(b) GROTESQUE
(c) INSIPID
(d) EVIL
(e) DASTARDLY

32. Place the letters in the grid to make drums and a boat.

ABCGENOOO

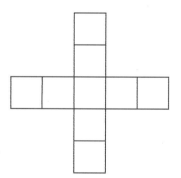

33. HARDWOOD is to APPLE
as SOFTWOOD is to:

(a) FIR
(b) BEECH
(c) PALM
(d) OAK
(e) WILLOW

34. If you were riding a HINNY, it be the offspring
of a:

(a) PONY + AN ASS
(b) HEIFER + A DONKEY
(c) STALLION + A SHE ASS
(d) PONY + A DONKEY
(e) ASS + A DONKEY

35. Fill in the missing letters to name a group of
horses.

_ A _ R _ S

36. Which circle's letters cannot be rearranged into a six-letter word?

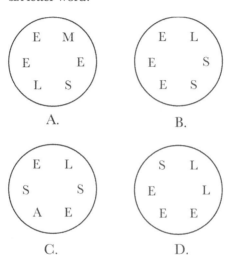

A.

B.

C.

D.

37. Find a one-word anagram.

LEMON ODE

38. Find a twelve-letter vegetable made up of two six-letter words—one inside the star, one outside the star.

39. Find pairs of letters to form four four-letter biblical characters—one pair is not used.

IN	EL	NO
AM	AH	AD
AB	AC	CA

40. Find the complete word that contains these middle letters. The word is hyphenated.

_ _ R F E T C _ _ _

1. Which is the odd one out?

A.

B.

C.

D.

2. Working counterclockwise, take one letter from each circle to spell out two antonyms.

Note: Each word starts in a different circle.

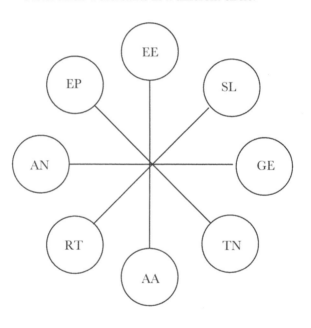

3. Which is the odd one out?

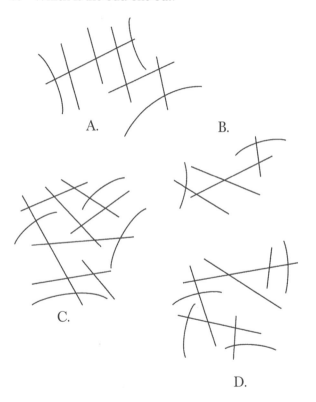

A.

B.

C.

D.

4. What two numbers can you place before all the three-digit numbers below so that all resulting five-digit numbers are divisible by 7?

$$976$$
$$661$$
$$381$$
$$- - \quad 864$$
$$927$$

5. Which figure below fits into the vacant space?

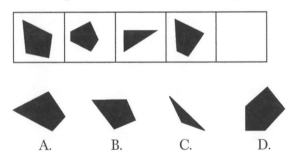

A.   B.   C.   D.

6. TITANIC VEER is an anagram of what eleven-letter word?

7. JAVELIN, MODULAR, LEXICON, MUTATED, ?

What word below continues the above sequence?

LIBERAL, BAROQUE, VOLUTED, LINOCUT, VENISON

8. 786395 : 658793

941682 :

  124968
  142986
  124986
  129486
  214986

9. Eliminate thirteen letters from the phrase below to leave a word meaning "suggested."

HIT THE NAIL ON THE HEAD

10. What do these words have in common?

RESTRAINED, DWINDLE, COUNTER-
SUNK, SKILLIGALEE

11. I am nine-letters long: 123456789.
My first four "1234" is to recognize.
My last five "56789" is a ridge.
My last four "6789" is a boundary.
What am I?

12. Imagine two bags. Each bag contains eight balls,
four white balls, and four black balls. A ball is
drawn out of Bag 1 and another ball out of Bag 2.
What are the chances that at least one of the balls
will be black?

A. 1 chance in 4
B. 1 chance in 2
C. 2 chances in 3
D. 3 chances in 4

13. Where would you put the number 10 in the grid?

1				8		
2		6				
3	5					
					9	
4			7			

14. Complete the following (two words):

_ A _ A _ A _ A _ A _

Clue: Isthmus

15. Add three consecutive letters of the alphabet to the group of letters below to form a seven-letter word.

FILY

16. Eight square pieces of paper, all exactly the same size, have been placed on top of each other so that some part of each piece of paper can be seen. Sheet A is shown completely and was, therefore, the last piece of paper to be placed. Which was the first piece of paper to be placed? Can this fact be determined?

17. Which two words are opposite in meaning?

AFFIRM, DELAY, RECANT, REFER,
CHANGE, OBLITERATE

18. What word is indicated below?

19. "A movement or course having a particular direction and character." Which word below does <u>not</u> fit this definition?

CURRENT, TENOR, TENDENCY, VOGUE,
DRIFT

20. Find a letter that replaces the question mark.

116 (O), 672 (S), 499 (F), 271 (?)

21. Which word is the odd one out?

BLITHERING
CATHEDRAL
WAREHOUSE
PROMETHEAN
STEPMOTHER

22. What number will replace the question mark?

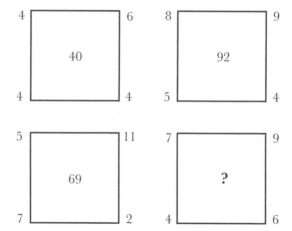

23. Which word should carry on the sequence?

GRUMBLE, EYELASH, HOLDALL, LOCK-NUT, TARRING, ?

(a) SKIMMED
(b) MIDLAND
(c) CLEAVER
(d) DUCTILE
(e) GRAPHIC
(f) HOLIDAY

24. What color is CINNABAR?

(a) PURPLE
(b) BLACK
(c) YELLOW
(d) BLUE
(e) VERMILLION

25. Simplify $\dfrac{1}{7} \div \dfrac{9}{14}$.

26. What is the meaning of ERUDITE?

(a) BULKY
(b) EFFERVESCENT
(c) SIMPLE
(d) LEARNED
(e) LOGICAL

27. If GAGGLE is to GEESE,
then MURDER is to:

(a) EAGLES
(b) PELICANS
(c) SWALLOWS
(d) CHAFFINCHES
(e) CROWS

28. Place four of the three-letter groups together to make two six-letter words.

LEG – LAW – GLE – END – OUT – GIN –
DED - MIS

29. Which of these is not an anagram of a ruler?

(a) MAZIN
(b) DRARIS
(c) PHILCA
(d) HALLMU
(e) ZAWRI
(f) GLIOATNI

30. Which two words have opposite meanings?

IGNOMINY, PASTICHE, COMPROMISE,
HUNGER, NICTITATE, HONOR

31. Find a six-letter word made up of only the
following four letters.

EN
LK

32. What number should replace the question mark?

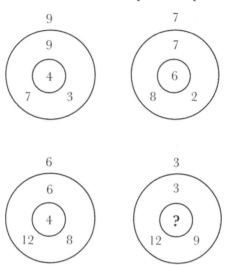

33. Place two three-letter groups together to make a six-letter word that is a cabin.

EPE - TEP - ANA - LAT - CAB - CHA

34. Which of these is not a fish?

(a) MOIDORE
(b) HALIBUT
(c) WRASSE
(d) FLOUNDER
(e) TURBOT
(f) LAMPREY

35. What letter should replace the question mark?

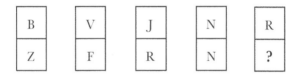

36. What is the opposite of SONOROUS?

(a) SLEEPY
(b) CAREFUL
(c) PHLEGMATIC
(d) FEEBLE
(e) SOFT

37. Rearrange the letters to find two seven-letter words that are synonyms.

Both words commence with the central letter.

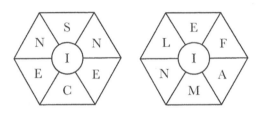

38. What is the name given to a group of MARTENS?

(a) EARTH
(b) ERST
(c) CLUTTER
(d) RICHNESS
(e) FLIGHT
(f) THICKET

39. Starting at an outside square and moving in any direction, spell out the ten-letter name of a tree.

IL	PT	LY
US	CA	KT
EU	BL	AC

40. HOTEL is to WAITER
as CIRCUS is to:

(a) TROUBADOUR
(b) LASCAR
(c) GRINGO
(d) FUNAMBULIST
(e) TOREADOR

TEST 16

1.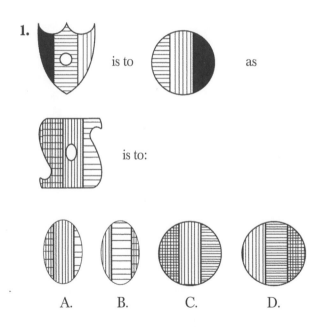

is to

as

is to:

A. B. C. D.

2. Which two words are opposite in meaning?

MALICE, BRAVERY, ECSTASY,
OPPRESSION, PRESTIGE, SUPPORT

3. Insert each of the letters from the phrase IDEAS
LOCATED into the grid once to find two
connected words.

Clue: Satanic supporter

4. What two numbers have the same relationship as 5963 : 810?

A. 7219 : 126
B. 5698 : 804
C. 2729 : 72
D. 1520 : 3040
E. 1234 : 765

5. Insert each of the letters from the words ONE DON REVVED once into the spaces below to complete a palindromic sentence—that is, one that reads the same backwards and forwards. For example: MADAM, I'M ADAM.

_ _ _ _ _ _ _ _ _ R _ _ E _

6. What phrase is indicated below?

7. Which pair of letters is the odd one out?

8. What number should replace the question mark?

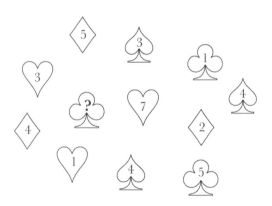

9. Complete the words to find five colors or shades. The initial letters of each can then be arranged to spell out a sixth color or shade.

```
_ N _ I _ O
_ M _ E _
_ A _ E _ D _ R
_ R _ A _
_ E _ O _
```

10. Which two words that sound alike, but are spelled differently, mean: LEND, SOLITARY?

11. What letter should replace the question mark?

12.

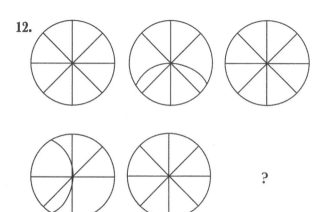

What contains the above sequence?

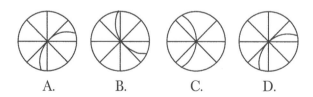

A.   B.   C.   D.

13. The words "in" and "out" are antonyms. Find two other words, one rhyming with "in" and one rhyming with "out," that are also antonyms.

14. What letter is two to the right of the letter immediately to the left of the letter three to the right of the letter immediately to the left of the letter C?

15. Three members of an ex-wives club were comparing notes. "I was married to James for just 9 months," said Trixie. "That's longer than me," said Davinia. "I walked out on him after 6 months." "Looks like I should have the prize for endurance then," said Helen. For how many months was she married to her husband?

16. Read around the tract in the direction of the arrow to find a fifteen-letter word. The overlapping letter appears twice. You must provide the missing letters.

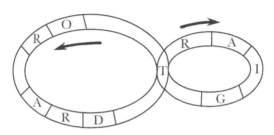

17. Which is the odd one out?

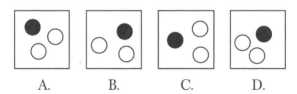

A.   B.   C.   D.

18. Add one letter, not necessarily the same letter, to the front, end, or middle of each word to find two words that are similar in meaning.

EARN LOG

19. All of the following words relate to business. Match up the words with their closest definitions below.

FLOTATION, INTANGIBLE, SYNDIC, FACTOR, TRANSACTION, LOGO, INCORPORATE, FLYER, MONOPOLY, FLAGSHIP

(i) Launching a business by means of a share issue
(ii) Trademark symbol or emblem
(iii) Exclusive control over a business activity
(iv) Deal
(v) Agent
(vi) Asset that has a value but no physical existence
(vii) Form into a registered company
(viii) Most impressive or successful product
(ix) Risky venture
(x) Representative, as of a university

20. Which is the odd one out?

A.

B.

C.

D.

21. Change the fraction to a decimal.

$$\frac{5}{16} =$$

22. What is the meaning of SHRIKE?

    (a) SHRINK
    (b) VEGETABLE
    (c) BIRD
    (d) FISH
    (e) DICE GAME

23. The vowels have been omitted from this quotation. Can you replace them?

THLNTCSHVTKNCHRGFTHSYLM

24. Z A P Y A W W H Y G U Y U S ?

Which letter should replace the question mark to continue the series?

25. If $4 \times 2 = 12$,
then $5 \times 5 = ?$

26. What number should replace the question mark?

 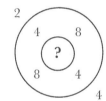

27. Place two of the four-letter groups together to make a word. The word is hyphenated.

IECE - TONE - TWOP - LEST - TAIL - BACS

28. Trace out a ten-letter word in any direction, using each letter once only.

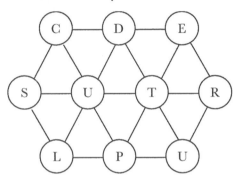

29. How many degrees are there in this angle?

(a) $128 \, ^4/_7°$
(b) $130 \, ^1/_7°$
(c) $133 \, ^3/_7°$
(d) $141 \, ^1/_7°$
(e) $146 \, ^3/_7°$

30. Which circle is most like E?
Is it A, B, C, or D?

E.

A.

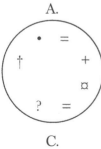

C.

D.

31. A word can be placed in the parentheses that has the same meaning as the words outside. What is it?

BIRD (_ _ _ _ _ _) GRUMBLE

32. Starting at an outside square and moving in any direction, spell out the name of a bird.

AR	PA	BU
IG	DG	RR
ER	US	IT

33. Place a word in the parentheses that when placed on the end of the first word makes a word, and when placed in front of the second word also makes a word.

BUTTER (_ _ _) FISHING

34. What number should replace the question mark?

26
41
17
6

38
26
41
17

70
38
26
41

22
70
38
26

10
?
70
38

35. If the missing letters in the circle below are correctly inserted they will form an eight-letter word. The word does not have to be read in a clockwise direction, but the letters are consecutive. What is the word and missing letters?

36. Find a one-word anagram for PEAS PAUL.

37. What fraction should replace the question mark?

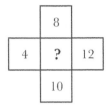

38. Which word means the fear of glass?

(a) NEOPHOBIA
(b) NELOPHOBIA
(c) DORAPHOBIA
(d) LOGOPHOBIA
(e) NECROPHOBIA

39. Find a twelve-letter nautical term made up from two six-letter words—one inside the star, one outside.

40. What temperature below is 104° Fahrenheit changed to Celsius?

(a) 34°C
(b) 36°C
(c) 38°C
(d) 40°C
(e) 42°C

1. What same three-letter word when inserted into the following letter combinations will make four new words? The word to be inserted must not be split and the order of the letter combinations must not be changed. For example: The word AND inserted into the letter combination HY makes HANDY.

ST
ARE
CHIE
SNER

2. What number should replace the question mark?

3. Which is the odd one out?

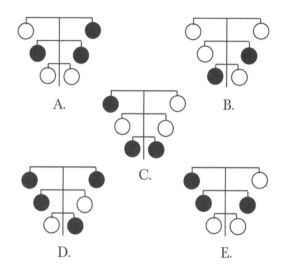

A.

B.

C.

D.

E.

4. Which is the odd one out?

ARCADIA, UTOPIA, ATLANTIS, AVALON, SHANGRI-LA

5. Insert the name of an animal into the bottom line to complete the three-letter words.

A	A	L	G	R	Y	P	O
R	S	E	A	A	O	E	A

6. Solve the cryptogram below. Each letter has been substituted by a different letter of the alphabet.

KM DWRVNVCR RSVMZC RSVC VC RSL GLCR DB KJJ FDXJEC. K WLC-CVPVCR BLKXC RSL CKPL RD GL RXTL.   —EDTY JKXCDM

7. Insert a word that can be tacked on to the first word and placed in front of the second to form two different words.

OUT		WAY

8. Moving clockwise, take one letter from each circle to spell out an eight-letter word meaning "complex." You have to find the starting point.

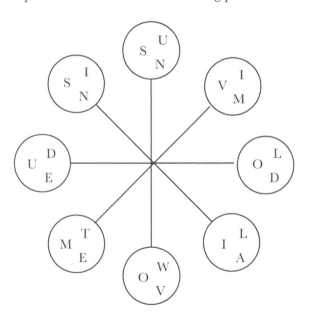

9. Which is the missing section?

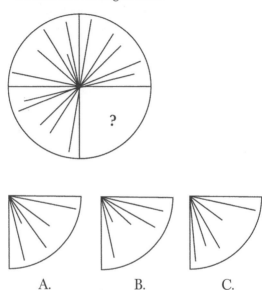

A.   B.   C.

10. Change one letter in each word to produce a well-known phrase.

FIT OF KISS

11.

2	6	9	4	7	8	1
4	1	8	2	3	9	6
9	3	7	6	1	4	2
8	7	3	?	?	2	4
7	8	1	?	?	6	9
3	9	6	7	4	1	8
1	4	2	8	9	3	7

Which four numbers below should replace the question marks?

| 6 | 1 |
| 3 | 2 |

A.

| 6 | 1 |
| 2 | 3 |

B.

| 2 | 1 |
| 6 | 3 |

C.

| 1 | 6 |
| 3 | 2 |

D.

| 1 | 2 |
| 3 | 6 |

E.

12. Spiral clockwise around the perimeter and finish at the center square to spell out a nine-letter word. The word starts at one of the corner squares. You have to provide the missing letters.

R	A	V
B	E	E
E	T	

13. Decipher each anagram to find two phrases that are spelled differently but sound alike. For example: A NAME, AN AIM.

TAUGHT HOST
TUFT SHAFT

14. I am causing an unctuous liquid to flow in contact with agitated bodies of a compound formed by portions of hydrogen and oxygen. What am I doing?

15. Taking the respective numerical position of letters in the alphabet, decode the following:
1183452018915131685

For example: LITTLE GIANT = 12, 9, 20, 20, 12, 5, 7, 9, 1, 14, 20 or 1292020125791420.

16. Each square contains the letters of a nine-letter word. Find the two words, which are synonyms.

		U	T	D
A	N	A	P	R
O	I	R	E	E
V	I	T		

17. Bill and Al share out a certain sum of money in the ratio 5:4 and Al ends up with $60. How much money was shared out?

18. Complete the five words so that two letters are common to each word. That is, the same two letters that end the first word also start the second word, and so on. The two letters that end the fifth word are the first two letters of the first word, thus completing the pattern.

```
_ _ O R _ _
_ _ E F _ _
_ _ L A _ _
_ _ N I _ _
_ _ L U _ _
```

19. Underline the two words inside the parentheses that the word outside the parentheses always has.

VOLCANO (SMOKE, ROCK, FUMES, WATER, CRATER)

20. What number should replace the question mark?

100   96½   89½   ?   65   47½   26½

21. Alter one letter in each word below to reveal a familiar phrase:

SOME GAS GOT GUILT AN I SAY

22. Moving through the doorways spell out an eight-letter word.

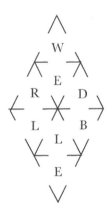

23. Simplify $\dfrac{825}{900}$ as a fraction.

24. Which word means the same as HAPLESS?

  (a) THREATENING
  (b) UNFORTUNATE
  (c) VAPID
  (d) CAPRICIOUS
  (e) OBTUSE

25. How many squares are there in this diagram?

26. Rearrange the two five-letter words to form a ten-letter word meaning "advanced fortification."

RABID HEDGE

27. Find the entire word that contains these middle letters.

_ _ _ NKYD _ _

28. Fill in the missing letters for the name of a group of animals.

_ E _ A _ E _ I _

29. Find a six-letter word made up of only the following four letters.

MG
ON

30. Which is the odd one out?

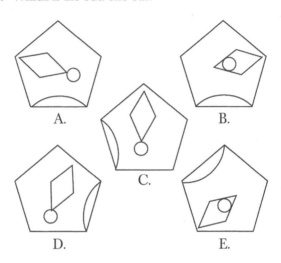

A.

B.

C.

D.

E.

31. Fill in the missing letters to complete the word.

_ _ G E W _ _ _

32. Place the letters in the grid to make a tree and a donkey.

ABBCOORRU

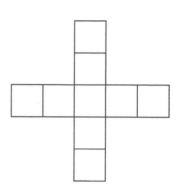

33. You have 60 cube blocks. What is the minimum number that have to be taken away in order to leave a solid cube?

(a) 27
(b) 29
(c) 31
(d) 33
(e) 35

34. If the missing letters in the two circles below are correctly inserted they will form synonymous words. The words do not have to be read in a clockwise direction, but the letters are consecutive. What are the words and missing letters?

35. Complete these musical terms.

B		U		S
A				A
S		A		E

36. What is the mathematical sign for factorial?

    (a) !
    (b) ≈
    (c) »
    (d) ∠
    (e) $\underset{=}{M}$

37. Starting from a corner square and continuing in a spiral to the center, fill in the missing letters to make a nine-letter word.

O	S	
	E	I
U	T	D

38. Which circle's letters cannot be arranged into a six-letter word?

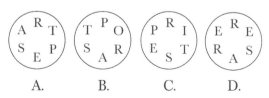

A.   B.   C.   D.

39.

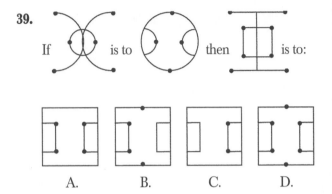

If [image] is to [image] then [image] is to:

A.   B.   C.   D.

40. What is kept in a BINNACLE?

(a) SAIL
(b) FLAG
(c) BALLAST
(d) COMPASS
(e) CUTLERY

TEST 1

1. INCOMPREHENSIBLE

2. 30. 7 × 4 + 2 = 30

3. PUITN = INPUT

4. D. The figure on the left arm goes inside the figure on the right arm. The remainder of the original goes inside the central figure.

5. WIT. WITLESS, WITNESS

6. All the figures are in anagram pairs except 294, which is therefore the odd one out:
563–635, 916–196, 298–829, 594–945, 752–572, 671–176, 832–283.

7. Laughing all the way to the bank.

8. ALLOT

9. LAUNCH SITE

10. 592. The numbers 48375926 are being repeated in the same order.

11. C. Each connected line of four circles contains one each of the four different symbols.

12. Take the bull by the horns.

13. 3. The numbers indicated by the hands increase by 7 each time—i.e., 12, 19, 26, 33.

14. NOTABLE, NOT ABLE, NO TABLE

15. (d) WET. Each letter moves forward four places in the alphabet.
S   TUV   W
A   BCD   E
P   QRS   T

16. 35. The numbers represent the position of each letter T in the sentence.

17. Tower of strength

18. 6. Each line of the four circles totals 17.

19. D. A facial feature appears in the center when it appears three times in the surrounding circles.

20. SAPPHIRE. These are all "blue" words.

21. D

22. (c) DESPAIR

23. Tutorial

24. C

25. MACKEREL

26. $^2/_5.$ $^5/_{11} \div {}^{25}/_{22} = {}^5/_{11} \times {}^{22}/_{25} = {}^2/_5.$

27. Overshadow

28. $^{29}/_{40}.$ Divide the top and bottom by 25.

29. (b) MUSOPHOBIA

30. (c) DINNER

31. PITCH

32. 36. We use a mathematical base of 10. If we use 8, we get $64 - 8 - 1$. $2 - 0$ (4×4 mod $10 = 16$), but 4×4 mod $8 = 20$. Therefore, $3 - 6$ (5×6 mod $10 = 30$), but 5×6 mod $8 = 36$.

33. C. A = CRYPTS,
B = LYRICS,
D = SCRIPT.

34. 6. In each vertical column the three smaller numbers equal the larger number.

35. (d) EXPERT

36. 44. $(8 \times 7) = 56$
$- (2 \times 6) = \underline{12}$
$= \overline{44}$

37. (b) TIERCEL (bird)

38. GUPPY, POPPY

39. (c) $\equiv$

40. LOCKJAW

TEST 2

1. SEPTEMBER
ANTISEPTIC
CENTIPEDE
MULTIPLE
JULY

2. 22. Each number is derived by adding the two numbers at either side of it.

3. MEAT, STEW, TART, SAGO, BEAN, FLAN, RICE.

4. WEDNESDAY

5. 3. All the other figures have an arrow pointing to their shortest side.

6. DEFT THEFT

7.

Seven pieces

8. 12

9.

27. Add digits of Circle 2 to obtain Circle 1.

Add digits of Circle 1 to obtain Circle 4.

Multiply digits of Circle 2 to obtain Circle 3.
Multiply digits of Circle 3 to obtain Circle 5.

10. 1. All widgets have a hole in the middle.

11. 12. $9 \times 8 = 72 \div 6 = 12$
$9 \times 4 = 36 \div 3 = 12$

12. All are buildings:
LODGE (OGLED),
TOWER (WROTE),
CASTLE (CLEATS),
TEMPLE (PELMET).

13. D. In all the others, the rectangle and black dot are at either side of the arrow. In D, it is the white dot and rectangle.

14. MA IS AS SELFLESS AS I AM.

15. (c) RISK

16. 315. Multiply by 0.75, 0.5, 0.25, and repeat.

17. 2. The numbers represent the number of rectangles in which they are inside.

18. GERMANE, COGNATE

19. "Many hands make light work."

20. LYCHEE

21. A. Now each line points to a different side or corner.

22. JACK

23. $6\frac{1}{4}$ $(5 \times \frac{1}{2})$ $\times$ $(10 \times \frac{1}{4})$

24. $33. Vowels = $4; consonants = $5.

25. 8. The corresponding segments of each circle add up to 19.
Example: $6 + 11 + 2 = 19$
$7 + 5 + 7 = 19$

26. REFEREES. The missing letters are R and F.

27. (c) 19.635 sq. in.

28. 63. $(9 \times 9) - (6 \times 3)$

29. (c) THROBBING

30. $\frac{1}{12}$;

$$\frac{\cancel{16} \times \cancel{9} \times \cancel{7} \times \cancel{2}}{\cancel{8} \times \cancel{18} \times \cancel{14} \times 12}$$

31. It is a wise father that knows his own child.

32. CORSAIR, FELDSPAR

33. C

34. D. The X is midway between a black and white ball.

35. ENUMERATE

36. (e) TENDON

37. 36. The differences are:
2^2 3^2 4^2 5^2 6^2 7^2

38. COMANCHERO

39. ANCESTRY

40. OVERFLOWS

TEST 3

---

1. Four ways.

2. THANKSGIVING

3. They all contain the letters

ONE in a certain position:

_ ON _ E _	_ _ ON _ E	_ O _ NE _
LONGER	BLONDE	CORNER
MONKEY	BRONZE	LOANED
WONDER	SPONGE	HORNET

4. B. This completes every possible arrangement of four blocks, not counting rotations and reflections.

5. C. SOFT

6. 2. In each pentagon,
$A + D = E + B + C$

7. Joe

8. 4146. In all the others, $A \times C = B$ and $B + C = D$. For example:
3 6 2 8
A B C D

9. OCCUPANT, RESIDENT

10.

11. SACRAMENTO (ESCORT A MAN)

12.

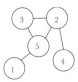

13. AC(CORD)IAN

14. ENERGETIC, LETHARGIC

15. RUSH

16. B. The figure is flipped over vertically.

17. ABALONE, ABANDON, ABDICATE, ABDOMEN, ABOUND, ABROGATES, ABSCOND

18. 12. Add up the three numbers and reverse—i.e., 7 + 8 + 6 = 21.

19. SLACK, TIGHT

20. D. The final figure at the end of each row and column is determined by the contents of the previous two squares. When a symbol appears in the same place in both squares it is carried forward but changes from cross to dot, and vice versa.

21. 32. Simplify:
5 + (8 ÷ 4) + (9 × 2) + 7
= 5 + 2 + 18 + 7 = 32
Order that must be taken:
× ÷ + −

22. FIFE, TUBA, LUTE, OBOE.
ODD PAIR: HA

23. PINION

24. JERKIN

25. JOSH, TEASE

26. C. This is the only ice-cream cone shaped figure that has two black circles in it.

27. A

28. BERBERIS, CAPSICUM, FOXGLOVE

29. CONE (NICK) KRIS

```
1   2    2 4 13 3  3  4
```
LISP (SOLE) ETON
```
1  2   2 4 13  3   4
```

30. (c) 400 ft. $(5^2 \times 16 = 400)$

31. 44. Start at 24, then add 6, then deduct 4 until spiralling in towards the center end.

32. (b) 720.   Take pi as $^{22}/_7$; then,
$^{22}/_7 \times 28 = 88$ inches
$= \dfrac{1760 \times 3 \times 12}{88} = 720$

33. ⊢ They are numbers 1 to 8 with the top and bottom horizontal lines missing.

34. (b) ∞

35. CHRISTMAS, MAURITIUS, FALKLAND

36. TEN

37. C

38. CABBAGE

39. DECK. QUARTERDECK, DECKHAND

40. D

TEST 4

1. F. All those with one black eye have their curl to the right. All those with a black nose have their curl to the left. All those with neither black eye nor nose have their curl pointing straight up.

2. Intelligently

3. AGE-GROUP, STOCK-STILL, BLOOD-TYPING, TWIN-SIZE

4. Minus $100

5. Least

6. 1. The top line plus the bottom line equal the middle line, i.e., 5384968 + 3276873 = 8661841.

7. AGATHA, to complete the sequence:

```
_ A _ _ B _
_ C _ _ D _
_ E _ _ F _
_ G _ _ H _
```

8. LET THE CAT OUT OF THE BAG

9. C

10. 10 provinces in Canada

11. ARMADA
WARMTH
CHARMS   XYZ = ARM
DISARM

12. 8. The sum of each column of numbers increases by 1 each time.

13.

S	O	L	S	L	O	S	O
S	O	S	O	S	O	O	S
O	O	S	O	S	L	O	O
O	S	O	L	S	O	O	O
S	O	S	L	S	L	L	O
L	S	L	O	O	S	O	S
O	O	O	S	S	O	O	L
O	S	L	L	O	S	L	O

14. A. It has only one loose end; the others all have two.

15. ORIGINATOR

16. 1. CAPACITY
2. BRAIN
3. EXPLORING
4. LEARNED

17. PENELOPE

18. 812. 6 + 2 = 8, 9 + 3 = 12

19. RETORTS (ORBIT) LIBERTY
2 5 1   1 2 3 4 5 4 3

20. A bolt from the blue

21. 20. 6, 5, 2, 3, 4. Opposite sides always add up to 7.

22. E. A is the same as C; B is the same as D.

23. (b) SAMOYED (dog). The others are:
  (a) QUETZALE,
  (b) CRUSADO,
  (c) BOLIVAR,
  (d) TESTER,
  (e) SESTERCE.

24. COASTER

25. HERMIT, NAUSEA

26. JITTERBUG, QUADRILLE, POLONAISE

27. LADYLIKE, HOYDENISH

28. SLUGGISH, INACTIVE. The missing letters are: S, G, C, and V.

29. X. Add $2 + 4 + 4 = 10 = X$

30. $11\frac{1}{2}$. There are two series $(+1\frac{1}{2})$ 7 $8\frac{1}{2}$ 10 $11\frac{1}{2}$

$(-2\frac{3}{4})$ 17 $14\frac{1}{4}$ $11\frac{1}{2}$

31. (e) SCARF

32. (a) ICOSAHEDRON

33. (d) 120°. $\dfrac{360°}{6} = 60°$

= Central Angle.

$180° - 60° = 120°$.

34. (e) BOAT

35. –2. $\dfrac{(4 \times 2) - 6}{7 - (4 \times 2)} = \dfrac{2}{-1} = -2$

36. RED

37. (e) CATS

38. SOUBRETTE

39. C. A = CAPSIZE;
  B = CREPES or CREEPS;
  D = PRECIS or PRICES

40. (e) FOOD

TEST 5

1. MAT
   * ✱ between words means anagram
   * ➤ between words means add a letter
   * ★ between words means change first letter

2. They all contain names of animals:
   A(MULE)T, D(EMU)RE, MO(RAT)ORIUM, MUL(TIGER)M

3. A. This completes every possible permutation of the original square where none of the four symbols occupy the position they held in the original square.

4. B. ESCAPADE

5. ICEBREAKER

6. He loved Vienna. He hated places whose names are made up of two three-letter words: MAD-RID, WAR-SAW, ANT-RIM.

7. 21. All the others are in 1:3 ratio pairs: 15–45, 9–27, 18–54, 8–24.

8.

8	6	2
4	T	7
5	1	3

9. VICUNA. All the others are man-made.

10. SLIDE RULE/SLY DROOL

11. RECLAIM, MIRACLE

12. 7.

	14			11
	2		6	
	⑦		4	10

13. B. The medium-size rectangle is moving from left to right at each stage.

14. WATER, MOVEMENT

15. C. It is a mirror image of the opposite square.

16. Nine. Thirty-one people pay $2.27 each. 9 × 31 = $70.37.

17. PEACE

18. G. Start at the left-side letter R and jump clockwise to alternate segments to spell out the word "regular."

19. 3205

20.

D E	M	P O F	B	I	S	O N	T
H	E B	M	Y I	Y	A	M O	A
S	E A	T O	O	A	S	R	T O

↑

Start at the letter indicated and spiral clockwise around the perimeter to spell out "mashed potato."

21. A

22. KHAKI, IGUANA

23. (a) .875. They read as follows: $\frac{1}{2}, \frac{2}{3}, \frac{3}{4}, \frac{4}{5}, \frac{5}{6}, \frac{6}{7}$.

24. (e) BALE

25. DUNLIN

26. $\frac{6}{7}$. $\frac{1}{3} \div \frac{7}{18} = \frac{1}{3} \times \frac{18}{7} = \frac{6}{7}$.

27. C. A   13 × 4 = 52
          37 × 10 = 370
          23 × 5 = 115

      B   22 × 4 = 88
          16 × 7 = 112
          17 × 8 = 136

      C   15 × 6 = 90
          24 × 6 = 144
          19 × 10 = 190, *not* 290

28. 1. S; it is the only letter not made of straight lines.

2. N; it is the only letter made up of straight lines.

3. D; it is the only letter not made of straight lines.

29. (c) CALABASH (fruit)

30. MISSEL THRUSH

31. The circles are in sets of three in different orders:

32. SLOWWORM

33. (a) HODOPHOBIA

34. CUR, RAT, APE

35. (c) 108°. $^{360°}/_5 = 72°$ = Central Angle. $180° − 72° = 108°$.

36. $3\frac{1}{2}$. $(5 × \frac{1}{10}) + (12 × \frac{1}{4})$

37. INGRAINED

38. $1365 =$

$$\frac{15 × 14 × 13 × 12 × 11 × 10 × 9 × 8 × 7 × 6 × 5}{1 × 2 × 3 × 4 × 5 × 6 × 7 × 8 × 9 × 10 × 11}$$

39. L is the same number of letters from E & S
B & V
G & Q

40. 0.375

TEST 6

1.

C	M	A	G	I
A	G	I	C	M
I	C	M	A	G
M	A	G	I	C
G	I	C	M	A

2. Hit the nail on the head.

3. 30 mph.
210 miles ÷ 30 = 7 hours
210 miles ÷ 35 = 6 hours

4. D. The rest are all the same figure rotated.

5. STUDY

6. GAUNT

7. IDENTICALLY ELECTING POET

8. SEPTEMBER. Start at JANUARY and jump one month, then two months, then three months, etc.

9. R. Take the left-hand letter from the top row with the right-hand letter from the bottom row added to ATE to spell EATEN. Then work left to right on the top and right to left on the bottom to spell out the words: EATEN, WATER, LATEX, HATED, DATED, GATES, and CATER.

10. 8. Looking along each row and down each column the sums of alternate numbers are the same. For example: $9 + 6 = 4 + 11$; $9 + 5 = 3 + 11$.

11. D. Working counterclockwise round the larger circles, the shaded quadrant moves one place clockwise. Working clockwise round the smaller circles, the shaded quadrant moves one place counterclockwise.

12. 150.
$38 \times 2 \,(+2) = 78$
$39 \times 2 \,(+2) = 80$
$58 \times 2 \,(+2) = 118$
$74 \times 2 \,(+2) = 150$

13. FACULTY

14. 24. The numbers, spelled out, follow the numerical sequence: 3-4-5-6-7-8-9-10. One, four, seven, eleven, fifteen, thirteen, seventeen. So the answer is 24—i.e., twenty-four = 10 letters.

15. GEORGINA. REIN AGOG is an anagram of Georgina; REAR LION is an anagram of Lorraine.

16. A. The red ball

17. ODD ONE OUT

18. B. In all the others the outer figure is the same as the inner figure.

19. STRATAGEM

20. MENDELSSOHN

21. 77. After the third number, each number is the total of the three preceding numbers.

22. 5.
$6 \times 9 = 54$ $54 - 5 = 49$
Similarly, $(7 \times 4) - 4 = 24$
$(3 \times 9) - 8 = 19$

23. APSE.
ROPE (PART) ANTE
3 1   1 23 4 2 4

SHAM (APSE) PIER
3 1   123 4 2 4

24. 15. We use a mathematical base of 10. If we use 7, we get $49 - 7 - 1$.

Therefore, $2 - 4$ (3×6 mod 10 = 18), but 3×6 mod 7 = 24.

$1 - 5$ (4×3 mod 10 = 12), but 4×3 mod 7 = 15.

25. 5.
$$\frac{24}{1 + 4 + 3} = 3$$

$$\frac{18}{1 + 4 + 1} = 3$$

$$\frac{30}{1 + 4 + 5} = 3$$

26. HILDEGARDE

27. POACH

28. (c) 10

29. MONEYMAKER

30. ODIOUS, MURDER

31. (d)

32. $7\frac{1}{2}$. There are two series:
$(+ 2\frac{1}{4})$ 1 $3\frac{1}{4}$ $5\frac{1}{2}$ $7\frac{3}{4}$
$(-1\frac{1}{2})$ 12 $10\frac{1}{2}$ 9 $7\frac{1}{2}$

33. ROUGHCAST

34. $\frac{27}{40}$. Divide the top and bottom by 25.

35. ADELE, ANNIE, ELIZA, ERICA

36. SIGNALMAN, GONDOLIER, MANNEQUIN

37.

  RQ ONM KJIH
S   P   L   G
+1, +2 +3

38. FUZZY-WUZZY

39. PIN

40. (b) 15

1.

2. B. A = DOE (EVIL-DOERS)
C = BEAR (BE ARMED)
D = EWE (BEJEWELLED)
E = APE (TRAP EASILY)

3. RECONDITE, DARK

4. 310. Looking around the circles:
2̇5 and 3̇2 = 84
  by adding 5 + 3 = 8
        2 + 2 = 4
3̇2 and 7̇3 = 96
  by adding 2 + 7 = 9
        3 + 3 = 6
7̇3 and 5̇1 = 88
  by adding 3 + 5 = 8
        7 + 1 = 8
Therefore: 5̇1 + 2̇5 = 310
  by adding 1 + 2 = 3
        5 + 5 = 10

5. SUPPORTER, ADVERSARY

6. B.

7. CLEAVER. It is a cutting tool whereas the rest are drilling tools.

8. C.

66	60
68	58

78	64	62	48	46	32
79	67	63	51	47	35
76	66	60	50	44	34
74	68	58	52	42	36
75	71	59	55	43	39
72	70	56	54	40	38

Move from 32 to 78 by the route shown in the sequence: +3, −1, +2.

9. Here today, gone tomorrow.

10. All have two meanings when spelled the same but pronounced differently:

APPROPRIATE (take possession of, suitable)

BOW (and arrow, to the King)

DESERT (leave alone, Sahara)

DOVE (dived, bird)

ENTRANCE (door, delight)

GILL (unit of volume, organ of fish)

LEAD (pipe, astray)

SLAVER (slave trader, drool)

11. 9.

$5 \times 3 = 15$ $3 \times 9 = 27$
$6 \times 2 = \underline{12}$
                27

12. B. The top half is folded over onto the bottom half.

13. C. The shaded figures represent 0.75 and 0.5.
$72 \times 0.5 = 36$
$68 \times 0.75 = 51$

14. HERE, THERE

15. C is missing to spell the word "circle."

16. CROSS-EXAMINATION

17. CHARLESTON

18. 37.5 minutes.
$$\frac{50 \times 6}{8} = \frac{300}{8} = 37.5$$

19. D. The third counter from the top disappears at each stage.

20. OFFICIOUS

21. (b) SILK FABRIC

22. ALUMINUM, MANGANESE, MAGNESIUM

23. DEPRESSED

24. C

25. REEL, so that it spells: 1-2-3. S<u>ON</u>, <u>EAT</u>, W<u>ORTH</u>, <u>REEL</u>.

26. D and E. They cannot be folded into a cube.

27. (c) ZINC

28. VOLATILE

29. OBSTETRICS

30. HOTELIER. The missing letters are H and L.

31. 142. The differences are:

1×19	2×19	3×19
19	38	57
4×19	5×19	6×19
76	95	114

32. MUESLI

33. 4. $(6 + 7 + 7 + 4) - (2 + 1 + 9 + 8)$

34. RED

35. PADDLING

36. (d) IRREVERENCE

37. WINTER CHERRY

38. The family that prays together stays together.

39. 9. $\dfrac{3 \times 7 \times 3}{7}$

40. JALOPY

TEST 8

1. A. The dot moves left to right at each stage first jumping one square, then two, then three. A square turns black once it has been visited by the dot.

2. 11. The right-hand circle contains the sum of pairs of digits from the three-figure number in the left-hand circle and vice versa— i.e., 378. 3 + 7 = 10; 3 + 8 = 11; 7 + 8 = 15.

3. SPEND, HOARD

4. GRIDIRON, WORKLOAD, FIREWOOD, MAINLAND

5. 468137. The even numbers and then odd numbers from the first number are placed in ascending order to form the second number.

6. They all contain the names of countries:

LIBERATION: IRAN;
INITIALLY: ITALY;
FRAGRANCE: FRANCE;
CHINCHILLA: CHINA;
SPEARMINT: SPAIN;
PERFUME: PERU;
CLAUSTROPHOBIA: AUSTRIA

7. W. It has twenty-two letters in the alphabet before it, and three letters after it.

8. GATEMAN'S NAME TAG

9. SPRING

10. Bend over backwards

11. 2. Looking both across and down, the sum of each pair of numbers is one more than that of the previous pair of numbers.

12. XYZ = RAP. RAPIDS, DRAPES, SCRAPE, ENTRAP

13. LONE, LOAN

14. F, J, J, N. They are the initial letters of the months of the year.

15. MINUET. All the words are dances.

16. D. All the others are made up of three identical figures; D is made up of four

17. GENEROUS, CHARITABLE, BENEVOLENT, KIND

18. IMPRISONMENT. The missing letters are P, N, and T.

19. VANISH

20. LLAMA, SKATE

21. MINE: MINERAL, EMINENT

22. SPITEFUL

23. (b) EXCITING. Each word commences with the last letter of the previous word.

24. PAJAMA

25. 0.875

26. (b) ULNA

27. HOSPITABLE

28. (c) ENTRAILS

29. AGE

30. (c) Cr

31. CLUTTER

32. HAMBURGER, MINCE-MEAT, SPAGHETTI

33. (d) MOUNTAINS

34. TOKEN.
    BATH   SALTS

GREEN   PEPPERS
ICE   FLOE
MAGIC   SQUARE

35. (e) DUMPLINGS

36. (d) DEACON

37. (b) PICTURE POSTCARDS

38. 2 hours.   6 hrs = $\dfrac{1}{6}$ = .166

3 hrs = $\dfrac{1}{3}$ = .333

Add .5

$$\dfrac{1}{.5} = 2$$

39. (c) CLUB SHAPED

40. 52. $(12 \times 5) = 60 - (4 \times 2) = 52$

TEST 9

1.

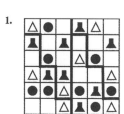

2. CHAPERON

3. 15. +0, +1, +2, +3, then repeated.

4. CUPID WAS THE GREEK GOD OF LOVE.
False; he was Roman.

5. 15 minutes

6. FASHION

7. LEXINGTON. The three-letter words formed are: NIL, ACE, MIX, OBI, TAN, SAG, CAT, WOO, BAN.

8. 90° in a right angle

9. SEVEN

10. MORBID HEAP

11. DRINKING FOUNTAIN

12.

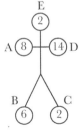

$B + C = A$
$A + B = D$
$(D + C) - (A + B) = E$

13. CRITICISM

14. They are all portmanteau words—i.e., words formed by combining parts of other words: GLIMMER (GLEAM, SHIMMER), CHORTLE (CHUCKLE, SNORT), MOTEL (MOTOR, HOTEL), FLOUNDER (FLOUNCE, FLOUNDER)

15. D. Add a point to an existing line, then add another line with the first arrowhead pointing to the left.

16. CLAVICLE

17. 7.

18. GALA – PAGEANT (NEAT – GAP)

19. Chain of command

20. Success is getting what you want. Happiness is liking what you get. —H. Jackson Brown

21. TOR. OPERATOR, TORUS

22. BURIED TREASURE

23. (e) 10^9

24. (a) ANTELOPE

25. GINKGO

26. OKRA, KALE, LEEK, BEET. ME is not used

27. (c) CHANSON (song). The others are: (a) CHIHUAHUA, (b) PAPILLON, (c) ELKHOUND, (d) SALUKI, (e) CORGI.

28. HEN, EMU, LOON

29. SEPARATE, DISUNITE. The missing letters are S, P, D, and N.

30. (d) NARROW NECK

31. Thirty-two

32. –35.
$$8 - (6 \times 7) - (10 \div 5) + 1$$
$$8 - \quad 42 \quad - \quad 2 \quad + 1 = -35$$
Order that calculation must be made in: × ÷ + –

33. HEEDFUL, OBLIVIOUS

34. C. A = LAPSES; B = PLACES; D = PLEASE.

35. 8. The numbers are in sets of 3 that add up to 20 each time.

36. KAMPONG

37. TOP

38. RHESUS MONKEY

39. 153. The differences are:

| –11 | –22 | –33 |
| –44 | –55 | –66 |

40. (c) ANNOYANCE

TEST 10

1. 1. Start with the 4 on the outer rim at the top. The total of each straight line of 4 numbers working clockwise is 9, 10, 11, 12, 13, 14, 15, 16.

2. VIGOR

3. OVER

4. D. Now each three adjacent blocks spell out a three-letter word: ADO, FOE, DOE, DUE, ELF, FEE, SEE, USE, SUN.

5. DETECTIVE STORIES

6. −1. $\dfrac{-7 \times 3 \times 2}{3 \times 2 \times 7} = \dfrac{-42}{42} = -1$

7. B. Starting at the top and working downwards, the third hexagon in each row of three hexagons is made up of everything in the previous two hexagons, except where the same component appears twice, in which case it is not carried forward.

8. CONCAVE, BULGING

9. He laughs best who laughs last.

10. FIRST. Each word contains three consecutive letters of the alphabet.

11. 6. $7 \times 3 \times 3 = 63$, $7 \times 5 \times 1 = 35$, $4 \times 2 \times 2 = 16$.

12. 13. The values are:

    ♢ 3

    ♡ 8

    ♤ 2

    ♧ 1

13. SUSQUEHANNA

14. On top of the world

15. GERTRUDE STEIN

16. BEECH, CEDAR, PLANE, MAPLE, LARCH

17. $^2/_7$. $^1/_4 \div ^7/_8$ = $^1/_4 \times ^8/_7$ = $^2/_7$.

18. 138, 135, 141, 138.
In each pair of rows:

A + C = F   B + D = G
A + D = E   B + C = H

A	B	C	D
E	F	G	H

19. 5935. In the others, the first two digits multiplied give you the last two digits. For example: $5 \times 7 = 35$ (5735).

20. WRY: DOWRY, WRYNECK

21. ELAND, REINDEER, ZEBU, ANTELOPE, BUFFALO. Sixth animal: ZEBRA.

22. (e) ZIGZAG

23. 6%

24. MICROSCOPE

25. (a) PLUMP

26. MIDSHIPS

27. DESTROYER, MINELAYER, TROOPSHIP

28. APHELION

29. 43. It is a series of prime numbers.

30. Seven at 50¢, three at $1.50, and two at $2

31. (e) 135°. $^{360°}/_8 = 45° =$ Central Angle. $180° - 45° = 135°$.

32. C. A is the same as D; B is the same as E.

33. (e) +

34. (c) SITOPHOBIA

35. 16 lbs. $(128 \div 8 = 16)$

36. SPRUCE

37. (c) 20°C. $68°F - 32° = 36° \times ^5/_9 = 20°$

38. (e) SLANG

39. PRONOUNCED

40. 120. 5 × 4 × 3 × 2 × 1

TEST 11

1. T(HAIL)AND

2.

G	R	A	D	E
R	I	L	E	D
A	L	I	B	I
D	E	B	I	T
E	D	I	T	S

3. Once. The vowel is E.

4. 3. 347 × 2 = 694; 489 × 2 = 978; 267 × 2 = 534.

5. RADIUS. It is in the arm; the rest are in the leg.

6. 7. All the numbers are the number of straight lines in each word.

7. FIRE
AFFIDAVIT
GRAVITATE
AGITATOR
LONGITUDE
SITUATION
WATER

8. 300. They are times in hours and minutes without the colon. Starting at 150 (1:50), move clockwise adding 35 minutes at each stage: 1:50, 2:25, 3:00, 3:35, 4:10, 4:45, 5:20, 5:55.

9. B. At each stage the third and fifth figures move to the end.

10. Might-have-beens

11. D. The vertical curved arms move from left to right and right to left, respectively, by an equal amount each time.

12. RATTLES

13. LARGE

14. PALINDROMICAL (I'M ON RAPID CALL). NURSE I SPY GYPSIES RUN is a palindrome.

15. 8. $6 - (3 \times 2) + (8 \div 4) + 6 = 6 - 6 + 2 + 6 = 8$.
Order that calculation must be made in: $\times \div + -$

16. 16. Start at 1 and move clockwise, jumping over two spaces and adding 3 each time.

17. C. It has only two small white circles, the rest have three.

18. LEAN, AND. WITH, THIN. GEM, EMIT. Musical word: ANTHEM.

19. 2 min., 15 secs. $(1.25 + 0.25) \times {}^{60}/_{40}$

20. $^{7}/_{40}$. Divide the top and bottom by 25.

21. KEYBOARD. Each word commences with the middle two letters of the previous word.

22. A. It spirals counterclockwise. The others all spiral clockwise.

23. 498. 6×83

24. (d) WHALES

25. (b) TAP

26. MINION

27. (e) MADRIGAL

28. WREATH, SENILE

29. SPOON

30. ATTIC, ERECT, CRYPT, AISLE

31. FRANGIPANI

32. SEASONED

33. (b) Σ

34. GAMIN, URCHIN

35. CONCH, LANCE

36. (a) OPPOSE

37.

A(bc)D(ef)G(hi)J
17(18-19-20)21(22-23-24-25)26(27-28-29-30-31)32

38. CATCHWORD

39. HER

40. GASTROPOD

1. Imagination

2. C. A has the same figures as D upside down; B has the same figures as E upside down.

3. Rub up the wrong way.

4.

86

Add lines into the position as shown in the original figure.

5. ALLAY, ROUSE

6. C. Some widgets have a straight edge.

7. 14. The numbers in boxes are the sums of two of the numbers in circles: 8 + 5 = 13; 8 + 9 = 17; 5 + 9 = 14.

8. OPPRESS, OPPOSITION, OPPORTUNE. Score a point for two correct. Score a bonus point for all three correct.

9. MEDDLESOME

10. BELL, HARP, LUTE, FIFE

11. B, so that each line across and down contains one each of the four symbols.

12. 24. Go counterclockwise around the circles and finish in the center. The first set adds 2 to each circle, the second set adds 3, the third set 4, and the fourth set 5.

13. PETULANT

14. SENILE FELINES

15. Seventeen

16. DAPPLE-GRAY

17. GRAND, GRAPH, GREAT, GUIDE, GUANO

18. SHEET-WRAP, LAPEL-TURN, NUT-CRACK, PAPER-WRITE

19. E. Opposite segments have lines in the opposite direction—i.e., horizontal becomes vertical and vice versa.

20. Purple. The colors start with the numerical position of each letter in the alphabet.

21. MAGNOLIA. HEM, SPA, PEG, PIN, TOO, AIL, SKI, TEA

22. 36. The differences are: $1\frac{1}{2}$ 3 $4\frac{1}{2}$ 6 $7\frac{1}{2}$ 9.

23. OVERTAKE. The missing letters are V and K.

24. (d) 102.

64	32	16	8	4	2	1
1	1	0	0	1	1	0

25. (d) ELLIPSE

26. –. They are in sets of four: × – + ÷.

27. BAR

28. 3E

29. 22. We use a mathematical base of 10. If we use 9, we get $81 - 9 - 1$.

Therefore, $2 - 6$ (6×4 mod $10 = 24$), but 6×4 mod $9 = 26$.

$2 - 2$ (5×4 mod $10 = 20$), but $5 - 4$ mod $9 = 22$.

30. $2\frac{1}{4}$. There are two series:

$(-4\frac{1}{4})$ 15 $10\frac{3}{4}$ $6\frac{1}{2}$ $2\frac{1}{4}$
$(+2\frac{1}{8})$ 1 $3\frac{1}{8}$ $5\frac{1}{4}$

31. (f) WISP

32. UNDERBID

33. (f) EPHEMERA (insect)

34. DACE, TOPE, ANGEL

35. RANSACK, RUMMAGE

36. (b) 59°F.
$15°C \times \frac{9}{5} = 27° + 32° = 59°F$.

37. Winning isn't everything, it's the only thing.

38. DISPATCHER

39. SCARAB BEETLE

40. ANTARCTICA

TEST 13

1. FINALE

2. JR. All the other pairs are the same distance from the beginning and end of the alphabet respectively.

3. ASK. DAMASK, ASKANT

4. A. The diagonal line moves one forward and two back at each stage. The dot moves two forward, then one back.

5. REVERENT

6. DIVISIBILITY

7. 1. In each pair of lines,
AG + CI = BH; DJ + FL = EK.
For example: 29 + 36 = 65;
28 + 63 = 91.

A	B	C	D	E	F
G	H	I	J	K	L

8. FEAR, SOME, WHERE,
EVER, MORE: FEARSOME,
SOMEWHERE, WHEREV-
ER, EVERMORE

9. BRIGANTINE

10. A. It contains four squares. The
number of squares in each figure
increases by one each time.

11. (i) ENCOUNTER
(ii) SEMINAR
(iii) FORUM
(iv) CAUCUS
(v) SUMMIT
(vi) CONFERENCE
(vii) AUDIENCE
(viii) RALLY
(ix) SYNOD

12. MEDIATE

13. PIE
DIE
DUE
HUE
HUMBLE

14. TRAFALGAR SQUARE

15. LESS

16. Up to a point.
Score a point for six correct
and a bonus point for all nine
correct.

17. ENACT.
NECTAR (ENACT) CARPET
2 1 4   1 2 3 4 5   3   5

18. A

19. MEATY.

CRAZY	GANG
APPLE	TURNOVER
FIRST	POST
CHINA	SEAS

20. TREBLE. All are music symbols.

21. $^{37}/_{40}$. Divide the top and bottom by 25.

22. C. Each row and column contains four black and four white dots.

23. 1 banana = 5¢.

$3a + 4b = 29$ $3a + 4b = 29$
$1a + 8b = 43$ $\underline{3a + 24b = 129}$ (×3)
(subtract) $20b = 100$
$b = 5$

24. 22 minutes before 12 noon was 11:38 AM. 70 minutes before it was 10:28 AM.

25. ORNATE, TEDIUM, UMPIRE, RECEDE, DEBTOR

26. PILLAGE, PLUNDER

27. D ♤

28. 0.0625

29. OBFUSCATE

30. PIQUET

31. TRIBULATION, HAPPINESS

32. IMPOSTER, DECEIVER. The missing letters are M, S, D, and V.

33. (a) YELLOW

34. BADMINTON, WRESTLING, BILLIARDS

35. 21.

$10 + (12 ÷ 4) + (2 × 9) - 10 =$
$10 + \quad 3 \quad + \quad 18 \quad - 10 = 21$

Order that calculation must be made in: × ÷ + −

36. DULCET, SWEET

37. (e) CYNOPHOBIA

38. SWADDLES, POCHARD, INITIALLY

39. DIHEDRAL

40. (c) BELIEFS

TEST 14

1. B. The symbol with the cross always moves to the opposite corner and the symbol occupying that corner moves across to the previously unoccupied space, taking the cross with it.

2. Center of gravity

3. Start at the H in the top left-hand corner and jump to alternate letters. After reaching the bottom right, return to the second letter on the top row and continue jumping to alternate letters to spell out the phrase "Here today, gone tomorrow." The missing letter is O.

4. 8. Add each of the numbers in the hexagon, then divide by 3 to get the number in the diamond.

5. DOUSED/DUE. All the others are paired whereby the three-letter words are spelled out by the second, fourth, and sixth letters of the six-letter words: AIL/FACIAL, NOD/UNFOLD, LID/ALLIED, RIM/TRUISM, USE/PURSUE, WAS/SWEARS, FEE/EFFETE, EAT/DEPART.

6. THE ANCIENT INHABITANTS OF THE AREA IN CENTRAL ITALY NOW KNOWN AS TUSCANY WERE CALLED ETRUSCANS. True.

7. B. Opposite segments are identical but with black/white reversal.

8. 30 min. 20 miles at 40 mph = $^{20}/_{40}$ × 60 = 30 min. 30 miles at 60 mph = 30 min.

9. Reinvent the wheel

10. WEASEL

11. ROALD AMUNDSEN

12. 47.

$7 \times 3 = 21 \quad 4 \times 9 = 36$
$63 \div 7 = 9 \quad 35 \div 5 = 7$

$2 \times 2 = 4$
$56 \div 8 = 7$

13. MINE, RUSH, DISC: Can all be prefixed by GOLD.
BOMB, ZONE, SCALE: Can all be prefixed by TIME.
BACK, SAIL, ASIDE: Can all be prefixed by SET.
WISE, WORK, TOWER: Can all be prefixed by CLOCK.

14. She originally had $99.98 and spent $49.99.

15.

2	8	5
4	6	T
7	1	3

16. A

17. $11\frac{3}{4}$. There are two series:
$(3\frac{1}{4}) \quad 2 \quad 5\frac{1}{4} \quad 8\frac{1}{2} \quad 11\frac{3}{4}$
$(-2\frac{1}{4}) \quad 12 \quad 9\frac{3}{4} \quad 7\frac{1}{2}$

18. MASTER, STREAM

19. 2. Primes: $29 + 37 = 66$
Squares: $4 \times 16 = 64$

20. CUSTARD PIE

21. GREEN

22. MUTUAL ADMIRATION SOCIETY

23. B. A is the same as D. C is the same as E.

24. It should be blank. Starting from the bottom right-hand corner, move counterclockwise in a spiral to follow the sequence:
1 2 3 4

25. SWEET

26. COMEDIAN

27. $2\frac{1}{2}$. $(18 \times \frac{1}{6}) - (6 \times \frac{1}{12})$

28. (a) BARS

29. FOIL

30. (d) $\sqrt{}$

31. (c) INSIPID

32. BONGO, CANOE

33. (a) FIR

34. (c) STALLION + A SHE ASS

35. HARRAS

36. D. A = MELEES;
B = LESSEE; C = LEASES.

37. MELODEON

38. MANGEL-WURZEL

39. CAIN, ABEL, ADAM,
NOAH. AC is not used.

40. FAR-FETCHED

TEST 15

1. B. This is the only one in
which the dot is not in both the
triangle and circle.

2. ENTANGLE, SEPARATE

3. D. In all the other figures, there
are exactly twice as many
straight lines as curved lines.

4. 31

5. A. All the figures contain one
right angle.

6. INTERACTIVE

7. LINOCUT. The vowels A, E,
I, O, U are being repeated in
the same order.

8. 124986. The positions of the
numbers change in the following sequence: (1 2 3 4 5 6)
9 4 1 6 8 2
(3 6 2 1 5 4)
1 2 4 9 8 6

9. HINTED

10. They are all weather words:
REST(RAIN)ED, D(WIND)LE,
COUNTER(SUN)K,
SKILLI(GALE)E.

11. Knowledge

12. D. 3 chances in 4. The possibilities of drawing the balls are black/black, white/white, black/white, and white/black. The only one of the four possible combinations where black does not occur is white/white. The chances of drawing at least one black ball is, therefore, three chances in four.

13.

Move as shown counting 1 space, then 2, then 3, etc. between numbers.

14. PANAMA CANAL

15. FIRSTLY

16. B. From top to bottom, the pieces are placed in the order: A, D, H, E, G, C, F, B.

17. AFFIRM, RECANT

18. NEWNESS: NE/W/NE/S/S

19. VOGUE

20. T. The letter that follows each number is the first letter of the number spelled out.

21. WAREHOUSE. All the other words contain THE.

22. 87. $(7 \times 9) = 63$
$+ (4 \times 6) = \underline{24}$
$ 87$

23. (e) GRAPHIC. Each word commences with the last letter of the previous word.

24. (e) VERMILLION

25. $\frac{2}{9}$.

$\frac{1}{7} \div \frac{9}{14} = \frac{1}{7} \times \frac{14}{9} = \frac{2}{9}$

26. (d) LEARNED

27. (e) CROWS

28. LEGEND, OUTLAW

29. (f) INTAGLIO (gem).
The others are:
(a) NIZAM,
(b) SIRDER,
(c) CALIPH,
(d) MULLAH,
(e) WAZIR.

30. IGNOMINY, HONOR

31. KENNEL

32. 3. $(12 - 9) \times (3 \div 3) = 3$

33. CABANA

34. (a) MOIDORE (coin)

35. J.

36. (e) SOFT

37. INCENSE, INFLAME

38. (d) RICHNESS

39. EUCALYPTUS

40. (d) FUNAMBULIST (tightrope walker)

TEST 16

1. B. The pattern follows the changing position of the sections inside the figure. The lines previously at the left move to the right. The lines in the middle move to the left and the lines at the right move to the middle.

2. ECSTASY, OPPRESSION

3. DEVIL'S ADVOCATE

4. A.
   7219 : 126. 7 × 2 × 1 × 9 = 126.

5. NEVER ODD OR EVEN

6. Shrinking violet

7. HP. Adding the numerical values of the letters in the alphabet, each pair of letters totals 26, except for HP, which totals 24.

8. 5. The numbers in each suit total 11.

9. INDIGO, AMBER, LAVENDER, CREAM, LEMON. Sixth color: LILAC.

10. LOAN, LONE

11. T. Start at A and move one place, then two places, through the alphabet, returning to the beginning of the alphabet after passing Z.

12. C. At each alternate stage, a line becomes curved, moving clockwise.

13. THIN, STOUT

14. F

15. 50 months. Take the Roman numeral value from the middle of each woman's name: TR(IX)IE, DA(VI)NA, HE(L)EN.

16. STRAIGHTFORWARD

17. C. In all the others, the black
circle is at the top.

18. YEARN, LONG

19. (i) FLOTATION.
(ii) LOGO. (iii) MONOPOLY.
(iv) TRANSACTION.
(v) FACTOR.
(vi) INTANGIBLE.
(vii) INCORPORATE.
(viii) FLAGSHIP. (ix) FLYER.
(x) SYNDIC.

Score a point for six or more
correct. Score a bonus point for
all ten correct.

20. C. It is a reflection of the others.
The others are all the same
figure rotated.

21. 0.3125

22. (c) BIRD

23. The lunatics have taken charge
of the asylum.

24. E. These are all three-letter

words: ZAP, YAW, WHY,
GUY, USE.

25. 41. We use a mathematical
base of 10. If we use 6, we get
$36 - 6 - 1$.
Therefore, $1 - 2$ (4×2 mod 10
$= 8$), but 4×2 mod $6 = 12$.
$4 - 1$ (5×5 mod 10 $= 25$), but 5
$\times 5$ mod $6 = 41$.

26. 3. $\dfrac{4 + 8 + 8 + 4}{(2 \times 4)} = 3$

27. TWO-PIECE

28. SCULPTURED

29. (a) $128 \, 4/7°$. $360/7° = 51 3/7° =$
Central Angle. $180° - 51 3/7° =$
$128 \, 4/7°$.

30. B

31. GROUSE

32. BUDGERIGAR

33. FLY

34. 22. Reading across, the bottom number in each column disappears and the other numbers drop down.

35. JUBILANT. The missing letters are J and L.

36. APPLAUSE

37. $\frac{1}{4}$. $4 \times 12 = 48 - 8 = 40$, $\frac{10}{40} = \frac{1}{4}$.

38. (b) NELOPHOBIA

39. SQUARE-RIGGED

40. (d) 40°C. 104°F − 32° = 72° × $\frac{5}{9}$ = 40°C

TEST 17

1. CAN. SCANT, ARCANE, CHICANE, SCANNER.

2. 6. $(23 + 31) \div 9 = 6$.

3. E. A is the same as C with black/white reversed. B is the same as D with black/white reversed.

4. ATLANTIS. The others are all imaginary places of perfection.

5. CHIPMUNK. The three-letter words made are: ARC, ASH, LEI, GAP, RAM, YOU, PEN, AND OAK.

6. An optimist thinks this is the best of all worlds. A pessimist fears the same to be true.
—Doug Larson

7. RUN

8. INVOLVED

9. A. Opposite segments are mirror images.

10. HIT OR MISS

11. D. The numbers 1, 3, 7, 8, 9, 4, 2, 6 are being repeated following the route shown.
(*See diagram on the top of page 346.*)

2	6	9	4	7	8	1
4	1	8	2	3	9	6
9	3	7	6	1	4	2
8	7	3	1	6	2	4
7	8	1	3	2	6	9
3	9	6	7	4	1	8
1	4	2	8	9	3	7

12. VERTEBRAE

13. THAT'S TOUGH, THAT STUFF

14. Pouring oil on troubled waters

15. ARC DE TRIOMPHE

16. VARIATION, DEPARTURE

17. $135. Al's share = $60
= 4 parts
Each part = $15
Original amount $15 × 9 = $135

18. CHORUS, USEFUL, ULLAGE, GENIAL, ALLUDE

19. ROCK, CRATER

20. 79. The differences are: $-3\frac{1}{2}$ -7 $-10\frac{1}{2}$ -14 $-17\frac{1}{2}$ -21.

21. ROME WAS NOT BUILT IN A DAY

22. WELL-BRED

23. $\frac{11}{12}$. Divide the top and bottom by 75.

24. (b) UNFORTUNATE

25. 55. $5 × 5 = 1$
$4 × 4 = 4$
$3 × 3 = 9$
$2 × 2 = 16$
$1 × 1 = 25$

26. BRIDGEHEAD

27. FLUNKYDOM

28. MENAGERIE

29. GNOMON

30. D. A and C are the same; B and
E are the same.

31. EDGEWISE

32. CAROB, BURRO

33. (d) 33

34. LAZINESS, IDLENESS.
The missing letters are L, Z,
L, and N.

35. BLUES, SNARE, STAVE,
BRASS

36. (a) !

37. DISSOLUTE

38. D. A = REPAST or PASTER;
B = PASTOR;
C = RIPEST or STRIPE.

39. D

40. (d) COMPASS

INDEX

(Italics indicate the answer pages)